The Beekeeper's Garden

THE BEEKEEPER'S GARDEN

Ted Hooper
& Mike Taylor

Alphabooks · A & C Black London

First published 1988 by
Alphabooks Ltd, Sherborne, Dorset
a subsidiary of A & C Black Plc
35 Bedford Row,
London WC1

British Library Cataloguing in Publication Data

Hooper, Ted

The beekeeper's garden.

1. Great Britain. Gardens. Plants.

Cultivation. Bee-keeping, for

I. Title   II Taylor, Mike

635'.0941

ISBN 0-7136-3023-X

Picture Credits

All photographs are by the authors except for the
following: Tony Birks-Hay pp. 3, 8, 19b, 45, 62, 71,
74, 88, 93, 104, 110, 117, 118, 132; C. de Bruyn 14,
15, 22b, 23; J. Miller 6; R. Pearce 18, 109. Line
drawings by Peter Haillay, Jackie Taylor (garden
plans).

Photosetting by Maggie Spooner Typesetting, London
Printed and bound in England by Remous Printers Ltd
and Bookcraft (Bath) Ltd

Contents

Introduction

The loving care which is lavished on the making and cultivation of personal, private, gardens is one of the idiosyncratic highlights of society in Britain, and few other countries. The gardens may vary in size from a window box to many acres, but in each case the pride of the owner is often equally strong. Many of these ardent gardeners watch what happens to their plants and become interested in the insects which are associated with them. In the last few years there has been a movement away from the 'kill everything that moves' syndrome, people being generally more interested in preserving wildlife rather than destroying it, and they are learning to differentiate between those insects that are beneficial, or neutral, and those which do sufficient damage to be destroyed as pests. In particular, many become interested in the bees, of all sorts, which are continuously working plants for nectar and pollen; and they come to understand the essential work the bees do in the production of seed and fruit, and recognize the value of their pollinating activities to the survival of wild flowers. In some cases this

A beekeeper's garden in Dorset. A variety of flowers to suit the bees.

leads to the. gardener becoming a beekeeper, so as to be more closely associated with these interesting insects, and to benefit from their labours of pollination and honey and wax production.

Conversely, many beekeepers who start as very poor and unconvinced gardeners become enthusiastic when trying to understand the difference in value of particular flowers to the honey bee, usually starting with field crops and the wild flowers of their area. These are the flowers which produce the beekeeper's honey crop, and most beekeepers become reasonably well informed amateur botanists. Interest then spreads to the flowers in their own garden, and close observation to decide which plants are most attractive to their bees. This is most important in suburban and urban areas, where the cultivated trees and flowers in private gardens and parks provide the only, or the largest proportion of, forage plants from which their bees will obtain nectar. Beekeepers will not only want to grow bee forage flowers themselves, but should try to persuade all their neighbours, the local council, parks department and highway authority to plant a reasonable proportion of bee forage plants, as this will be a very significant factor in the size of their honey harvest. In fact, urban and suburban areas are very good for

7

honey production, their crop varying less in size from year to year than do honey crops in rural districts.

In the following pages we are offering the basic information required by bee-keepers who wish to increase the value of their garden to honey bees, and by gardeners who wish to take up beekeeping and have some colonies of honey bees in the garden. Hopefully we shall introduce some newcomers to these two absorbing and rewarding crafts. Anyone thinking of starting beekeeping is recommended to join the local beekeeping association and to attend their meetings, which in the winter will provide talks by well known beekeepers, and in the summer garden meetings where they will see colonies handled and discussed. They will meet local beekeepers who will give very useful help and advice, and suggest sources of bees. Even the established beekeeper is well advised, if moving to a completely different part of the country, to contact the local beekeepers and find out what the beekeeping is like, because climatic conditions and forage type and availability can vary widely from place to place. Established beekeepers who wish to upgrade their gardening are advised to join their local garden society, and to attend gardening classes at their local college, as this will bring them in contact with other local gardeners. The societies usually supply seeds and sometimes plants at a reduced price, and organize exchange of plants between members. Whether you are starting bee-keeping or gardening, do not just take the views of one person only, but talk to as many as you can and get a consensus of opinion.

The beekeeper's reward — a frame of stored honey.

1 For the new beekeeper

Colonies of honey bees can be kept successfully anywhere: beekeeping is practised from the centre of the largest cities to the depths of the countryside. But when keeping honey bees the most important consideration must always be that the bees are not a nuisance to one's neighbours or the passing public. There is no reason why they should be; honey bees do not interfere with anyone when they are away from the hive. They are defending the colony when they cause trouble, and conditions should be so arranged that their instinct to defend is not aroused. If a quiet strain of bee is correctly sited and looked after with care and consideration for neighbours as well as the welfare of the colonies, and the number of colonies installed kept at a reasonable level, then there is no reason why the neighbours should come into contact with the bees at all. Strains of honey bees can be obtained which are so quiet that they will not try to sting the beekeeper when the colony is being taken apart during manipulation. These strains have to be looked for, and advice from an experienced beekeeper in the district should be sought regarding local sources. Let no one convince you that bad-tempered bees make most honey, it is quite untrue. Of the many hundreds of strains of honey bees that I have worked with, the two

finest, both for honey production and quality of colony, were so quiet that they did not sting unless trapped and squeezed, inside a sleeve for instance. Good-quality, hardworking and quiet strains of honey bees can be obtained, and are a pleasure to work with.

First get your bees

The new beekeeper can start up in one of three ways: by buying a colony of bees, or a nucleus of bees, or by obtaining a swarm of bees. In beekeeping terms a 'colony' is a unit containing at least six, but usually ten or eleven, combs covered by adult bees, including a laying queen honey bee, and containing all ages of the young stages — that is, eggs, larvae and pupae. A 'nucleus' is a small colony usually containing four combs covered with bees, a young laying queen and young of all stages (the collective name for the young is 'brood'). A swarm is a collection of bees, about 10,000 in number, and a queen, which has left a colony and is on its way to set up a new home. It has no combs or brood. The swarm can be collected by a beekeeper and given or sold to the new beekeeper.

I would recommend starting with a nucleus bought from a reputable beekeeper or equipment supplier. A full-sized colony is an awesome sight to a tyro, no matter how docile it is, and a swarm is usually of unknown origin and you do not know what you are taking home: their temper may leave a lot to be desired, and they could be diseased. A nucleus is a complete little colony which does not overawe the beginner, and if bought from a reputable source it will be docile, easy to handle and free of important diseases. As the nucleus grows larger and becomes a colony, so does the beekeeper's ability to handle bees and his or her understanding of bee behaviour, so that happenings which might at the beginning have been rather off-putting will be accepted as normal and not a cause of worry.

Where to put the hives

When colonies of honey bees are brought into a garden the first decision that has to be made is where they shall be sited. If the owner is a new beekeeper there are a number of things about the behaviour of bees that must be understood. The colony must be brought in from at least three miles away, otherwise your bees will fly over some of the landmarks they flew over from their previous site, and this will cause them to follow their old flight lines to their former home. Honey bees do not orient afresh each time they leave the hive. It is not necessary in natural conditions, where they will be in a hollow tree or a cavity in a cliff, which is certainly not going to move around. They learn the position of their colony during the first few days of their lives, and that is sufficient in natural conditions. Bees belonging to a beekeeper, however, may be subjected to having their colony moved around, sometimes over considerable distances, and have to re-orient and learn a new set of flight lines

each time they are moved. However, many of the older bees may rush out of the hive without realizing they are in a new position and be lost, unable to find their way to the new home. To mitigate this effect it is well worth while lightly stuffing the entrance of a newly moved hive with fresh green grass, which will emphasize to the bees that something is different. It will slow up exit from the hive until the grass has withered and the bees can clear it away. Once honey bees have flown from a new position they will have learned their new flight lines and local landmarks, and will accurately return to the hive entrance. Should the beekeeper then decide the hive would be better in a different position in the garden, and move it ten feet or more, the bees going out will not realize they have been moved and on the return journey will use the flight lines they have just learned, returning to the place where the hive entrance was before it was moved. Many will cluster on the ground at this spot, and die. The particular strain of bee affects how many will fail to find their hive only a few feet away, but in any case many will be lost and the colony will be considerably set back in development. The old beekeeping rule that 'Bees should be shifted under three feet or over three miles' is a good one to remember and follow.

When a nucleus or colony of honey bees is brought into the garden, therefore, it must be put on its permanent site before the bees are allowed to fly. You cannot put them somewhere 'for the time being' while you make up your mind where they should be placed permanently. If you do, you will have the job of shifting them three feet a day until they are in the right place, or have to leave them where they are until winter when, after a week or two of very cold weather, when the bees have not flown, it is possible to shift them across the garden to their new site. Nor can you have

A small swarm, or cast, hanging in a cluster while scouts search for a new home.

the bright idea of keeping them confined in their box or hive until you have made up your mind. Colonies should be shut in for as short a time as possible, or many bees, or the whole colony, will die. Nuclei can be kept shut in for longer periods, but during this time they need careful attention. They should be kept in the cool and in the dark if possible, and when they begin to buzz loudly a cup or two of water should be poured, through the top screen, over the bees. It is better to decide on their position before they arrive, and put them in the right place straight away, and the box opened to let them fly.

If the beekeeper is bringing swarms into the garden then they also must be hived on their permanent site right away. They learn their new position as soon as they fly from a hive they have accepted as suitable. If there is something they do not like about the hive, or, more likely, if they are small

swarms (called casts or afterswarms) which have come out of a colony several days after the first swarm has left, and usually contain more than one unmated queen, they will leave the hive and hang up again as a swarm. The first swarm out of a colony each year, the prime swarm, usually has the old mated queen from the colony and will settle happily into any hive provided. The main difference with swarms is that they can be hived at a new position in their original apiary, and only a few of the older bees will return home to their old colony. The bees' behaviour patterns cause them to remain in a new position once they have swarmed (although in nature they will usually fly some way away from their old colony before setting up home in a new cavity).

So, the new beekeeper bringing bees into the garden, or the established bee-keeper moving to a new home, must first

11

decide where the bees are to be sited and should, if possible, prepare the apiary site before the bees arrive. It will be much more difficult to work around the hives when they are in position. Establishing the apiary requires two decisions: the position of the apiary in the garden, and the layout of the hives in the apiary.

The size of the garden and the closeness of neighbouring houses will, of course, affect where you site the hives. The apiary should be enclosed by a hedge, and should be sited as far from neighbours as possible. A very large plot in a rural setting will pose no problem. The bees can be sited away from the boundaries and in a position where they cannot overlook the garden from the entrance of the hives. This can be made certain by a low hedge of about 3-4 feet (about 1 metre) high, which will also suffice to act as wind shelter for the colonies. In a small suburban, or urban, garden it will be best to enclose the colonies, or the garden, in a hedge about 6 ft (2 m) tall, thus pushing the flight lines of the bees up above head height before they leave the garden. This is necessary because bees do fly into obstacles, particularly ones that are not always there, and people may think they are being attacked when in fact it is a quite accidental collision. In heavily built-up areas, once the bees are pushed up by a high fence they will be kept high by the houses, and only those actually working the flowers will descend into the gardens. In a rural setting, however, bees will fly low to the ground when it is windy, and will even fly around under the lee of a hedge to go through gaps or gateways in considerable density. This behaviour should be thought about when siting, and care taken that this does not happen where roads, footpaths or other rights of way exist. It may be possible to produce a new gap for them to fly through in a more convenient place (see the chapter on planning).

Temporary fences can be of wattle or a small-meshed plastic, such as greenhouse shading. These materials last a few years, giving time for hedging plants to be planted and to become established, and are very efficient in pushing the bees up and providing a windbreak. A living hedge, however, is the most attractive and efficient way of fencing off the apiary, and the type of plants to use, their planting and pruning is dealt with in Chapter 3. Hedges provide better conditions for the colonies than walls, as these produce considerable wind turbulence close by. Wind coming through a hedge reduces the strength of the turbulence and pushes it some way back from the hedge. If colonies are placed 3 or 4 feet (1-1.25 m) from the hedge, and with the entrance pointing at the hedge, the bees will have calm air in which to slow down and enter the hive.

How many colonies?

The number of colonies which may be kept in an apiary will depend upon the type of area and the density of human population surrounding it. Two is the minimum number of colonies which may conveniently be kept, one colony on its own is a liability because when things go wrong, and they surely will, you have nothing from which to draw to repair it. With two colonies mistakes or natural problems can often be repaired by taking from the unaffected hive. Two is also the maximum, I would suggest, when setting up a new garden apiary in a built-up area. This will be enough to find out how the neighbours will view the project when they realize you are keeping bees. If the climate of opinion permits, one can soon increase the numbers to suit one's enthusiasm and space. For two reasons I would suggest that four or five colonies is about the maximum which should ultimately be kept in a built-up area. Above this number the bees become more generally visible as they search around the hives in times of little forage, take cleansing flights in spring (leaving little yellow spots on washing), and later in the season large numbers of young bees fly around making orientation or play flights. The second reason is that there may be far more beekeepers around in the immediate area than you would imagine, and too high a density of bees will reduce the possible crops of honey for everyone. There is only a finite amount of nectar available in an area, and the ideal stocking rate will be one that is just able to harvest this nectar and turn it into honey; too many bees will reduce the crop per colony and increase the cost of production, and too few bees will fail to collect some of the nectar and leave it to be consumed by the yeasts which live in the nectaries. There is no way of calculating the potential of an apiary — it can only be tested by practical experience. Remember it can vary from year to year and during different times of the same year. In rural districts, on larger plots of land, more colonies can be kept, the number depending upon the proximity of neighbours and on the overstocking problem, which will be affected by the land use of the immediate neighbourhood. Most experienced beekeepers will agree that the maximum number in a permanent apiary in most areas of Britain should not be greater than about 12 to 15 colonies; the present agricultural practices have so reduced the density of bee forage throughout the year that it does not provide subsistence for more.

The size of the apiary and the way the colonies are set out in it will depend upon the number of colonies involved and the amount of spare land available. Ideally, the two-colony apiary should have the colonies 6 feet (2 m) apart to give the beekeeper room to work and perform manipulations such as artificial swarming, and have them facing in opposite directions to minimize drifting of young bees into the wrong colony. This would require an area of 13 x 6 feet (4 x 2 m) inside the hedges. This may not be available, and although two colonies can be accommodated in as little as 4½ ft square (1.3 x 1.3 m), manipulation is then made very difficult. My advice would be to get as near the ideal as possible. As the number of colonies on a site gets larger the problem of drifting becomes more severe. It occurs mainly when young bees are out on orientation flights and fail to return to the right hive. This causes colonies to become unbalanced, reducing the average crop from the apiary, and rapidly spreads disease from colony to colony. It is at its greatest when colonies are sited in a straight line, all facing the same direction, and at a minimum when the hives are placed in a circle, all facing a slightly different aspect. Siting twelve colonies in a circle would require an apiary of some 31 ft square (9.5 x 9.5 m), or if arranged in two smaller circles an area of 29 x 18 ft (8.8 x 5.5 m) would suffice. When placed in two or more clumps of hives bees will drift to places where the picture they see is repeated; this happens to returning foragers as well as young bees, and can be reduced by planting single small trees or shrubs in the apiary to act as landmarks. In all cases the hives should be arranged so that when you are working on one, with the hive open, you are not standing in the flight line of a nearby hive, or trouble will ensue, not necessarily to yourself if the bees are docile, but it may initiate robbing between colonies, especially towards the end of the honey flows. Particularly in the case of a large apiary, there should be a good hard path between it and the place where the honey is to be extracted, so that a wheel-

barrow, or better still a small two-wheeled truck, can be used at harvest time to convey the full boxes from place to place.

A well laid out apiary, where plenty of space is available. The box on the right is a solar wax extractor, used to recover beeswax from comb.

What sort of hive?

My own choice of hive would be the Modified Commercial, but certainly a single-walled hive and not the old-fashioned WBC. Although the latter may be more decorative, it is more conspicuous than the former type, takes up more room, both when manipulating and for storage of parts not in use (all the extra pieces have to go somewhere), and is not as flexible in use, needing modification before some manipulation techniques can be used.

The hives should be placed on stands and, to avoid backache and for ease of manipulation, these are best of such a

The Modified Commercial hive

wth which, if left un-
uned, produces an unholy
ngle. The size of the flowers
minishes, all produced at the
p of the plant.

There are two ways to
une, depending on the vari-
y of clematis you have. Those
at flower early and late in
e season need gentler prun-
g (eg, 'Nelly Moser', 'Marie
isselot', 'Lasurstern' and
uble 'Vivyan Pennell').
ard pruning removes all the
der wood and, with it, the
st flush of flowers. So this
ar cut any unfamiliar clema-
back to 6-8ft, generally
ying it up at high level and
king out any dead wood.
u may find you are cutting
f shoots several inches long
hich have already started to
rout at the top of the plant,
t don't worry about that.
runing will encourage more
luable shoots low down.

If it then flowers in June and
eptember, prune the same
ay next year; you have an
rly flowerer. If it only flow-
s in August-September, it is
late-season-only clematis,
nd can be pruned down hard
2ft in February/March.

ush roses

he rose bushes which require
articular spring pruning are
e modern large-flowered
ybrid tea) and cluster-flow-
red (floribunda) roses. Large-

grow anywhere between 3ft
and 6ft and produce their
flowers in bunches. (Old-fashioned English roses can be left
alone at this time of year.)

Both kinds of bush roses
need to be made to produce
plenty of vigorous new wood
low down in the bush, and
therefore they can be pruned
hard now, always cutting just
above an outward pointing
bud. Expect to take away two-
thirds of the plant, leaving the
strongest new shoots at a third
of their length, and cutting out
some older stems at the base.
Thin, wispy growths may be
cut out entirely.

Stocky single-flowered roses
like 'Peace' and 'Ruby Wed-
ding' can stand the hardest
pruning, and may be taken
down to 12 inches. The taller
cluster-flowered roses like 'Ice-
berg', 'Mountbatten' and *The
Times* Rose' are better treated
more gently, leaving a framework 2-3ft high.

The most vigorous, such as
'The Queen Elizabeth', which
will grow to 8-10ft, need to
have old wood taken out low
every year, to keep young
wood coming from the base.
Without such attention they
quickly get taller and taller,
and woodier and woodier,
until the whole thing has to be
cut down in spring.

STEPHEN ANDERTON

Pruning may seem difficult

Learn the art of bee-keeping in Pulborough, West Sussex, next weekend

A five-colony apiary using the minimum of space.

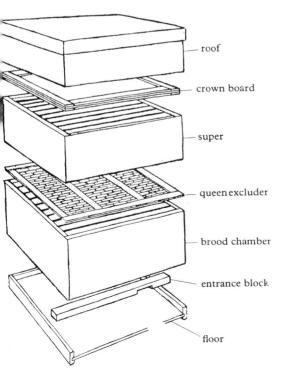

roof

crown board

super

queen excluder

brood chamber

entrance block

floor

height that one can stand at ease with one's knuckles resting on the top of the brood chamber. This allows the removal of combs from the brood chamber for examination without bending, and is conducive to good handling, with little jarring or crushing of bees to annoy the colony. Stands are of many varieties, and my own preference is for one made of 2 x 2 in (5 x 5 cm) pegs driven about 12 in (30 cm) into the ground, with rails of the same material nailed on the top. Single stands should have rails about 20 in (50 cm) long, double stands 4½ ft (1.3 m) long. Double stands are the more stable and the most useful in the long run, and need support only one colony. The height of the stands should be about 16 in (40 cm), but should be adjusted to suit the beekeeper's height.

In Europe many beekeepers keep their colonies in 'bee houses'. This has been little practised in Britain, although it was

15

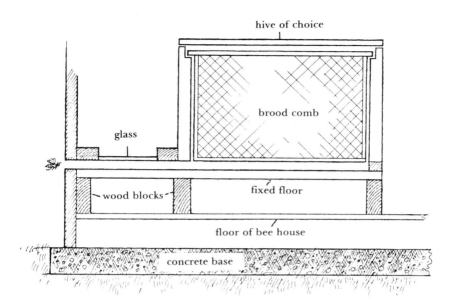

This type of entrance to a hive in a bee house allows the use of standard hives, and gives room to twist boxes apart when manipulating.

more popular a century or so ago, but recently it has been suggested as a suitable method of beekeeping for urban and suburban conditions. The suggestion has merit for several reasons: colonies are well protected and inconspicuous, but, more important, they can be manipulated at almost any time and in any weather. This has considerable advantage in the urban context, where it is essential to prevent colonies swarming and so possibly annoying neighbours. Manipulations can thus be done on time and are not at the mercy of the weather. A small shed of about 8 x 6 ft (2.5 x 2 m) would accommodate three to six colonies, three on each long side, and the construction of the bee entrance which I have used is shown in the diagram. Using ordinary hives, I prefer this to the continental method of placing the hives against the wall, which makes it difficult to separate the boxes when working the colonies.

Water requirements

Honey bees require a lot of water throughout the year, except when a nectar flow is
in progress, when they have a surplus
which has to be evaporated off. They need
the water to add to the stored honey so that
they can eat it and, in very hot weather, to
cool the brood in the hive. They prefer to
take the water from places where it is in
small quantity and can warm up, and seem
to prefer dirty water to clean. They will,
however, collect water from garden ponds,
and even from swimming pools, which
makes them highly unpopular with the
owners of these amenities. It is therefore
essential, particularly in a built-up area, to
provide the bees with a water source, and
to see that they use it. Probably the best is a
drum of water with a tap, or a small hole,
which can dribble onto a sloping board
with a herring-bone arrangement of slats
to guide the water (see illustration). Bees
can be enticed to use it by filling the drum
with a very weak sugar solution, but once
they have found it plain water is sufficient.
If you can encourage moss to grow on the
board the system will be more efficient in
holding the water. You could, of course,
build your own garden pond and put
plenty of plants in it so that the bees would
have plenty of surfaces to stand on while
drinking, and not far to swim should they
fall in. They could be introduced to your
pond by putting a few saucers of weak
syrup around its edge to attract the bees
into the vicinity.

A simple water supply for bees. The water
trickling down the herring-bone of slats soon
begins to grow moss, which adds to its
attractiveness to the bees.

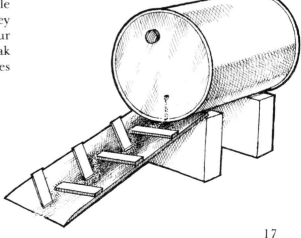

17

A worker bee foraging for nectar by thrusting its tongue into each individual floret of the composite flower. The bee has picked up pollen all over its body from the outer ring of open florets.

2 Bee and beekeeper

Above: the three types of honey bee in a colony: the male drone on the left, the queen in the centre and a worker on the right. Below: as the beekeeper would see them on the face of the comb. One of each type is ringed: drone at bottom, queen in the middle, and worker at the top. Most of the others will be workers, but there are a few more drones.

Although this is not a book which sets out to deal with practical methods of bee-keeping, this chapter will give a brief resumé of the life of the honey bee, the events of the beekeeping year and what time the beekeeper needs to spend working the colonies. It will of necessity be very brief and beekeeping beginners should get a book giving more detailed information to guide them during their handling of the colonies.

The honey bee's life

The honey bee starts off as an egg laid in one of the cells of the honey comb. The eggs are laid by the queen, which has the ability to fertilize the eggs or not as she lays them. Unfertilized eggs develop into males, called drones, whilst fertilized eggs produce females. There are two sorts of honey bee female: a fully sexually developed female, the queen, and a smaller female, the worker, which is incapable of mating although in special circumstances can lay a few eggs — which develop into males. The two sorts of female are termed castes. The queen mates during the first three weeks of her life, and is incapable of doing so again. She is mother of all the individuals in the colony, and can lay eggs

19

A comb taken from a colony, showing the normal distribution of honey at the top and sides, and a circular patch of sealed brood in the centre. The open cells between the white honey capping and the darker cappings of the brood will usually contain stored pollen.

at a rate of 2000 or more a day during peak periods of laying. The eggs hatch in three days to produce larvae, legless white grubs curled up in the bottom of the cells. The larvae are fed by the worker bees and grow rapidly until, at the end of eight to ten days, depending upon sex and caste, they are sealed in the cells by the workers with a domed wax capping. The larvae change into pupae and emerge as adults a few days later.

The normal honey bee colony comprises one queen, a large number of workers and, during summer, 500 or so drones. The population of workers varies with the time of year, from 5000 to 10,000 in winter and 30,000 to 60,000 in mid summer. This fluctuation of population is a major economic feature of the honey bee colony in the temperate areas of the world. The large summer population can work the

Large fully-fed larvae in their cells. The walls of the cells have been cut back to give a better view. Larvae of this size would be sealed or capped within a few hours.

20

flowers and store a large amount of honey surplus to their immediate requirements. This store can then be used by a much smaller population to provide it with food during the winter when no, or a very few, flowers are available.

The workers, as their name implies, do all the work of the colony, doing indoor jobs for about their first twenty days, and then becoming foragers working in the field for the rest of their life — about another fifteen days. During this indoor period they produce beeswax and use it to construct the comb; they feed the brood, eating pollen to produce a sort of 'bee milk'. Workers take the nectar from incoming foragers, and convert it into honey by evaporating off most of the water and converting complex sugars to more simple ones. By this contact with the foragers they are themselves stimulated to begin foraging on the same plants, going out with complete details of the forage, position and distance from the hive, and the taste, smell and sugar concentration of the nectar. Few bees look for flowers, most are directed by the 'bee dance' to a specific crop.

Foragers fly out to collect four substances. The first, nectar, is processed into honey, and both these substances are composed mainly of sugar and water, and provide the energy which the bee needs for its daily life. Some sugar is converted by glands into beeswax, and much is converted by muscles into heat to keep the colony warm. A smaller number of foragers collect the second substance, pollen, the main food of the bee, providing its proteins, vitamins and mineral requirements. A variable number of bees collect water with which to dilute the honey and to cool the hive, and some collect a substance from plant buds called propolis, or bee glue, which is used to varnish over the inside of the hive, stop up any holes and glue down anything movable. Workers will

Queen emerging from a queen cell via the small trap door she has cut in the end.

mount guard and defend the colony whenever this is necessary, but only when it is necessary. During quiet times there is little evidence of watchfulness.

At normal times the bees are inhibited from producing new queens by a glandular substance, termed 'queen substance', produced by the reigning queen. As the queen gets older her production of queen substance reduces, or as the colony grows in population the amount of substance is insufficient to keep the workers inhibited and they produce new queens, not in the normal hexagonal cells but in specially constructed, hanging, acorn-shaped queen cells. When this happens the colony can accept a new queen, the old one dying or being killed, or more frequently they split up and produce one or more new colonies. This is swarming. It is the only way a colony can reproduce and become two or more colonies. The old queen, being

The beekeeper's year

The art of beekeeping is to work with the honey bee and use its inherent patterns of behaviour to persuade it along the lines you wish it to take. Persuasion rather than compulsion is the rule; it is difficult, and painful, to try to make a bee do anything it doesn't want to do.

The beekeeper's year starts in September when the colonies are got ready for winter, aged queens are replaced and it is assured that the colonies have sufficient stores to last them through the winter: those that are short are topped up with sugar syrup. Having prepared them correctly for winter the colonies can be left untouched until the following spring. Except in special circumstances the hives will not be opened again until the weather has warmed up and temperatures have reached 50°F (10°C)

Above: Examining a comb. The beekeeper's hand is holding a hive tool which is used to prise the boxes and frames apart. Below right: Removing a super which has been used as an extension brood chamber. The picture clearly shows the population size of a good colony. At the bottom right can be seen the corner of the queen excluder, which is used to separate the brood area (and the queen) from the honey storage areas above.

capable only of laying eggs but in no way being able to look after them, has to leave, accompanied by a good number of workers to set up a new colony in a new home. The normal procedure is for a swarm to come out of the hive and hang up near by for a time, while some workers fly off to find a suitable place to set up the new nest. Having found a new home the swarm flies off to it and becomes a new colony.

At the end of the season, when flowers become very scarce, the queen stops laying and the colony settles down to endure the winter. Towards the end of winter the queen starts laying once more, and when eventually spring flowers appear the colony begins to expand once again.

once more. On a nice spring day the beekeeper will don a veil, light the smoker and open the colonies to see how they are progressing. At this time of year the main job is to discover any problems the colonies may have, and to use one's skill to get rid of the cause and to build them up to optimum condition. As colonies expand, boxes of comb are added to the hive for the bees to spread into.

Once colonies are built up to full size they are then liable to swarm unless steps are taken to prevent this happening. Preparations within the colony for swarming can occur any time from the first week of April to the end of July, and the event itself will depend upon the timing of the local flowers and the constancy of their succession. Some of the earliest swarms I have had were in suburban apiaries where a constant succession of flowers bloomed from snowdrops onwards. Methods of swarm prevention and control will be found in any good beekeeping textbook and should be carefully studied and used. It is essential for good-neighbourly relations, and for the productivity of your colonies, that colonies are prevented from swarming, particularly in urban or suburban situations. After the swarming period the colonies are given additional shallow supers to accommodate the honey, if there is a nectar flow on, until the flows peter out and no surplus is being stored. The supers of honey are cleared of bees and taken away for the honey to be extracted from the comb and put into containers for storage.

The beekeeper is now ready to prepare the colonies for winter once more. On average, beekeepers check their colonies once every seven to ten days during the active season, whichever is most convenient, and this means that they see them opened about twelve to fourteen times in a year. A competent beekeeper should need

more or less ten minutes to manipulate a colony, while two working together need only three minutes. This is the minimum time needed. You may take longer while you are learning, or because you are interested in looking at things in the colony which are not really of practical importance in producing more honey. One thing to remember: always enjoy your beekeeping, never let the hive numbers rise until the job becomes drudgery, or keep bees whose temper reduces your satisfaction at opening a hive and looking at the bees.

A routine examination of the brood chamber by well protected beekeepers.

3 Hedges

An apiary with a high Leyland cypress hedge to push the bees up above the neighbouring property. The sycamore tree gives a landmark for the bees returning to the apiary.

The beekeeper's garden may contain a boundary hedge running around the whole garden, or a hedge surrounding the apiary alone. Either or both of these could be found necessary, depending upon local circumstances. The usual reason for surrounding the apiary with its own hedge is to push the outgoing forager bees up above head height to prevent them coming into contact with your neighbours. Secondary advantages gained by the use of an apiary hedge are:

1. Providing a sheltered hive exit and, even more important, a sheltered entrance so that the bees, returning heavily laden on bright but windy days, are not blown to the ground, which they may be unless they can decelerate through calm air.

2. A reduction of the wind chill factor. This can mean a reduction in the amount of stores used up in a severe winter. During the spring it will allow the colonies to send out foragers at a lower temperature than if they were unprotected.

3. Preventing the guard bees overlooking the rest of the garden and being attracted by movement of people walking around or working nearby.

If the garden is protected by a boundary hedge the colonies may be placed in a convenient corner and should be sited about 3 feet (1 m) from the hedge, and facing into it. This will push the bees up before they leave your premises, but they may curl back over the hive and fly at a low level across your own garden. Should you wish to push them up in your garden as well, it will be necessary to provide a hedge at the back of the hives. If space is limited then a narrow barrier will do. One way of doing this is to erect a fence of not more than 2 in (5 cm) mesh wire or plastic netting supported by posts. A *Clematis montana* or some similar plant (I have seen runner beans used in this way) could be planted to climb over the wire. The bare stems provide sufficient cover in winter, and when in leaf and flower the coverage is quite dense enough to prevent 'fly-through' during the busy summer season.

Most of the flowering plants recommended for hedging in the past were, in fact, used around large estate apiaries where space was not limited and pruning, as we know it, was hardly necessary. This meant that plants such as holly, *Viburnum, Berberis*, willow, laurel, *Pyracantha, Escallonia* and many others produced large numbers of flowers right on the bees' doorstep, as it were. Today, even the largest private gardens do not have sufficient space to allow us to effectively use plants in this way. If they are pruned regularly then it is unlikely there will be any quantities of flowers produced, so do not take this flower-value too much into account when choosing a hedge, although some partial exceptions are listed.

Plants with dense twiggy growth and persistent leaves provide the best shelter, but this does not mean your hedge has to be a conifer — there are many other evergreens suitable for hedging. In addition, beech, when trimmed, also retains its leaves and makes one of the very best of all hedges, but is very slow growing. Some of the plants recommended for hedging may suffer in colder districts, whilst nearer coastal areas they may flourish — e.g. *Rosmarinus*.

Clipping

The uneven growth of unclipped hedges is anathema to most gardeners, and clipping back, usually twice a year, will be necessary if a neat appearance is to be maintained. Shears have traditionally been used for clipping, but the advent of the cheap electric hedge trimmer (hopefully connected to a circuit breaker) has reduced the incidence of this pleasant sound of summer. Plants with large evergreen leaves such as laurel should be 'pruned' with secateurs, not clipped, to prevent mutilating their leaves, which discolour badly. Evergreens (including conifers) should never be pruned between October and March,

otherwise the 'sheltered' leaves below the pruning cut may be scorched by sun or wind and killed by frost. Remember, too, that regular pruning (for frequency see the table below) does more than anything else to prevent bare basal sections developing at the bottom of the hedge — something that must be avoided at all costs, since it both reduces the shelter effect and encourages bees to fly through rather than over the hedge.

As with most other hardy plants today, a hedge can be established at any time of year, since the bulk of plants are now grown in pots. The traditional bare-root (no soil attached) plants can still be obtained, and will be considerably cheaper than those grown in pots. The planting season for these will, however, be shorter — November to March in Britain — and the choice will (and should) normally be limited to deciduous subjects. Some evergreens can be obtained bare-root and although cheaper than their pot-grown counterparts usually do not establish themselves as quickly.

A good hedge will protect an area effectively up to ten times its own height. So for our average garden of, say, 70 x 40 ft (21 x 12 m) a 5-6 ft (1.5-1.8 m) hedge should be more than adequate for the sides, while a 7-8 ft (2-2.5 m) hedge will be required for the end(s).

If at the end of the day you decide you cannot afford the space for a hedge, then use larch lap fencing. This will provide adequate shelter in much the same way as a hedge and be a fairly neutral foil or backdrop for your plants.

The plants listed in the following table are really a short list of those suitable for the average garden, and which will be trimmed for shape and height. This will largely upset the plant's normal growth habit, but I have still shown this against each plant, for information.

Plants suitable for hedging

Hedging plant	growth rate	type	habit	planting distance	pruning	comments
Buxus sempervirens (Box)	slow	🌿 evergreen	⟂ erect	1 ft / 30 cm	1 x yr	Not so popular now due to its slow growth, but makes an excellent aromatic hedge, perhaps attaining 5 ft (1.5 m) in 7-8 years. Try one of the variegated cultivars.
Carpinus betulus (Hornbeam)	medium	deciduous	◯ rounded	1 ft / 30 cm	2 x yr	Rather like beech but faster growing — looks good when mixed in with beech.
Chamaecyparis lawsoniana (Lawsons Cypress)	medium	🌿 evergreen	⟂ erect	2 ft / 60 cm	1 x yr	Raised from seed, so more variable and interesting than Leyland Cypress. Many cultivars — grey, gold, etc — available.
Cotoneaster horizontalis (Herringbone Cotoneaster)	medium	deciduous	≡ horizontal	3 ft / 90 cm	1 x yr	Excellent for planting against a fence or wall, where it will grow erect and flower and berry freely.
Cotoneaster lacteus	medium	🌿 evergreen	weeping	18 in / 45 cm	1 x yr	Rather lax habit but can be 'tied in' to canes or wires. Flowers and berries well in spite of being trimmed.
x Cupressocyparis leylandii (Leyland Cypress)	fast	🌿 evergreen	⟂ erect	3 ft / 90 cm	2 x yr	Very fast grower with dense habit. Rather dark and sombre but provides exellent shelter. Try the golden form 'Castlewellan'.
Ligustrum ovalifolium 'Aureum' (Golden Privet)	medium	🌿 evergreen	◯ rounded	1 ft / 30 cm	2/3 yr	A first-class hedge with good colour.
Prunus 'Cistena'	slow	deciduous	◯ rounded	1 ft / 30 cm	1 x yr	Similar to *Cerasifera* 'Pissardii' but more dense in growth and less vigorous. Leaves bright red, flowers white.
Prunus laurocerasus (Cherry Laurel)	fast	🌿 evergreen	◯ rounded	2 ft / 60 cm	2 x yr	Unlikely to flower when trimmed, but the extra-floral nectaries may encourage you to plant one of the many cultivars.
Pyracantha (Firethorn) 'Orange Charmer' or 'Mojave'	medium	🌿 evergreen	⟂ erect	2-3 ft / 60-90cm	1 x yr	Can make a stunning hedge when lightly trimmed, with berries well into the winter. An ideal hedge.
Rosmarinus officinalis (Rosemary)	medium	🌿 evergreen	⟂ erect	1 ft / 30 cm	1 x yr	Choose one of the more upright cultivars such as 'Miss Jessup's Variety' or 'Pyramidalis'. Very light trimming to encourage its erect habit. Coastal or mild areas only.
Thuya plicata 'Atrovirens'	medium	🌿 evergreen	⟂ erect	2 ft / 60 cm	1 x yr	Very dark green shiny leaves with pleasant fruity smell. Excellent backdrop for brightly coloured flowers.

Key

- ⋎ — deciduous
- 🌿 — evergreen
- x yr — number of pruning 'trims' per year
- ⟂ — erect growth
- ◯ — rounded shape
- 〰 — weeping
- ≡ — horizontal growth

4 Planning your garden

Very few of us will be fortunate enough to have a completely bare plot on which to have our wicked way; and even if we did the pressures of moving into a new house, coupled with the necessity of at least doing 'something', combine to ensure that the resultant something is usually less than the ideal we had in mind.

It is in fact simpler to take over an existing garden which can be moulded over the years to fit your own ideas and requirements. However bad you think such a garden is, do not be tempted to dig up everything, for there are very few gardens that do not have some redeeming features. Building up from some existing tree or shrub will save you time and money, and will help to give a degree of maturity to your garden which might otherwise look rather spartan for a few years — even fast-growing plants such as *Forsythia* will take 3-4 years to develop a rounded mature form from its gaunt early form.

The following pages in this short section will not make you an expert in garden design — no book can — but hopefully they will help you come to a decision about what to do and how to set about doing it.

Deciding what you want

Firstly, take a walk in your own locality, as this will tell you which plants might grow happily in your own garden. Look at as many mature gardens of your own garden size as possible. Note down the features and plants that you particularly like and may wish to incorporate. Try to repeat this exercise at different seasons (if you have the time and patience), for there are many gardens that look wonderful from June to September, with their summer bedding plants and roses, but thereafter are a disaster aesthetically and provide no early or late bee forage.

Think carefully about the number of trees in other people's gardens and see how much shade these create, for this will affect not only which plants will grow beneath them but also the number of visiting bees and the location of your hives.

Also, before proceeding further you will need to decide if you are going to grow vegetables and/or fruit. These are normally grown separately, and since most people find they are less pleasing to the eye they may need to be screened off (see section on hedges).

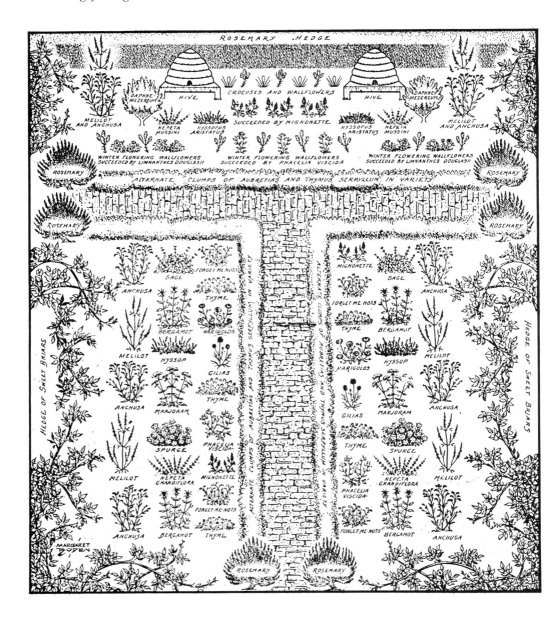

Bee gardens are no new thing. This old garden contains many herbaceous plants designed to interest the bees from the two traditional skeps at the top of the picture.

As a result of your neighbourhood excursions you should have arrived at some conclusions about which plants you would like to grow, and what features you wish incorporated in your own garden. Decide also if you would like a formal garden, which basically amounts to having beds, borders and lawns with straight edges (see Plan 1), or an informal one with gentle curves (see Plan 2). The informal approach is now the more common, since it looks more natural and relaxing, especially on the small rectilinear plots which are almost inevitable with newer houses. The two approaches are not mutually exclusive and many happy compromises exist. For a detailed planting scheme of the border at top right of Plan 1, see Plan 3.

At this stage several different options present themselves for consideration (the two main ones are described below), but whichever you choose do not let anyone or anything (except other beekeepers or this book advising on the suitability of your choice as it relates to beekeeping) interfere with your selection of plants, or you will almost certainly end up with an unhappy mixture, including double-flowered forms, which may be more decorative but will be of little use to your bees.

Remember not to plan your garden with the plants placed all around the edges, for nothing is more boring than being able to see every detail of it from the house — gardens should be designed so you just *have* (through curiosity if nothing else) to walk round them, and, if you have done a good job, there should be something interesting to see at every twist and turn.

If you decide to have proper paths, or if you have created 'desire lines' (areas where people are drawn to walk, for example towards a garden seat) then make sure your hives and associated flight paths are situated a reasonable distance away. Better still, pick the best possible location for your hives and then create your paths and desire lines accordingly.

Putting plans into action

Option 1 Hand your design requirements and plant lists over to a professional garden designer. This is obviously the most expensive approach. The designer could be local or you could send the details to a mail-order design service. This is bound to be cheaper but is unlikely to be as complete and appropriate as the work produced by a local expert, who will visit the site before drawing up a plan. Many design firms (not mail order) offer a complete service and will prepare the ground, obtain plants, plant them, lay slabs and carry out all associated work. Make certain that you get a detailed estimate and that you read the small print of any contract you sign, for you will usually be expected to accept substitutes where your specified plants are unobtainable.

If you have chosen this option then you should still read on, as you can then judge more readily the quality of the service you receive.

Option 2 Draw up your own plan, using the hints given below and on the following pages, and either obtain the plants and do the associated work yourself or ask a local firm to do all the work, or at least the heavy part of it, for you; ask around amongst friends and neighbours to find someone with a good reputation.

Drawing your plans

A sheet of plain A3 paper (approx 16½ x 11½ in or 42 x 29 cm) will allow you to use a scale of 1 in to 6 ft (1 cm = 72 cm) for an

Plan 1 — Formal garden design

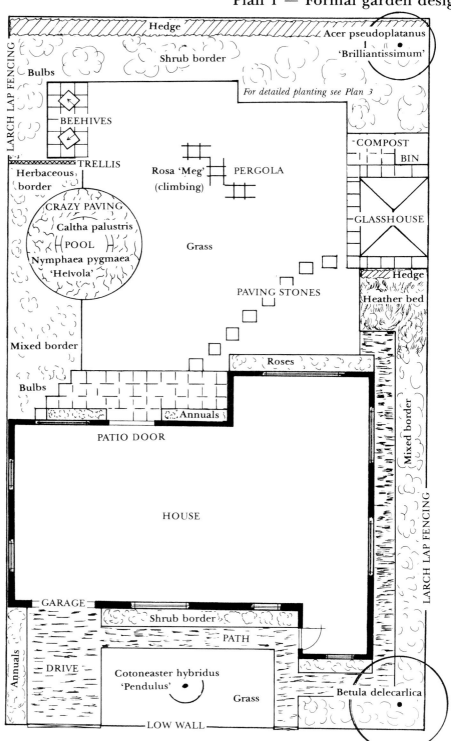

Hedge

Acer pseudoplatanus
'Brilliantissimum'

Shrub border

Bulbs

LARCH LAP FENCING

BEEHIVES

For detailed planting see Plan 3

COMPOST
BIN

TRELLIS

Herbaceous
border

Rosa 'Meg'
(climbing)

PERGOLA

GLASSHOUSE

CRAZY PAVING

Caltha palustris

POOL

Grass

Hedge

Nymphaea pygmaea
'Helvola'

PAVING STONES

Heather bed

Mixed border

Roses

Bulbs

Mixed border

Annuals

PATIO DOOR

HOUSE

LARCH LAP FENCING

GARAGE

Shrub border

PATH

Annuals

DRIVE

Cotoneaster hybridus
'Pendulus'

Grass

Betula delecarlica

LOW WALL

Plan 2 — Informal garden design

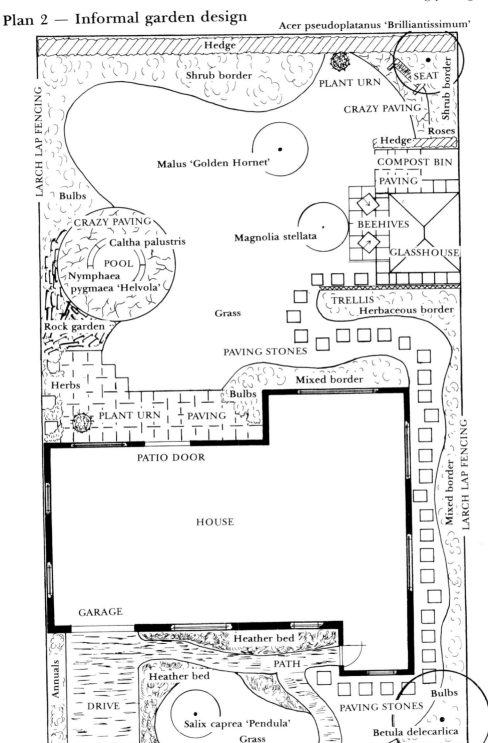

Acer pseudoplatanus 'Brilliantissimum'

Hedge

Shrub border

PLANT URN

SEAT

Shrub border

CRAZY PAVING

Roses

Hedge

Malus 'Golden Hornet'

COMPOST BIN

PAVING

Bulbs

BEEHIVES

CRAZY PAVING

Caltha palustris

GLASSHOUSE

POOL

Magnolia stellata

Nymphaea
pygmaea 'Helvola'

TRELLIS

Herbaceous border

Grass

Rock garden

PAVING STONES

Mixed border

Herbs

Bulbs

PLANT URN

PAVING

PATIO DOOR

HOUSE

LARCH LAP FENCING

Mixed border

GARAGE

Heather bed

Annuals

PATH

Heather bed

DRIVE

Bulbs

Salix caprea 'Pendula'

PAVING STONES

Grass

Betula delecarlica

31

above-average sized garden on a plot of 90 x 50 ft (27.5 x 15 m). Two such gardens (incorporating some existing features) are illustrated in Plans 1 and 2, showing distinctly different approaches to garden design on the same plot.

Once you have established the outlines of the various borders, patios, etc. (taking care not to have too many sharp or awkward corners which might make lawn mowing difficult) decide which plants or groups of plants will be placed in the various locations. Use the keys and descriptions in Chapter 5 to find plants that suit the scale and sun/shade aspects of your garden. Large, medium and small forms of most genera are given. Group smaller plants in threes or fives as necessary to give reasonable impact and balance; for example, if you want to plant *Erica* species near a rhododendron, you will need several plants to make any impact at all.

In conclusion, I would repeat again that reading books will not make you into a garden designer. However, if you follow the basic ground rules as set out here and apply these to your personal tastes (and whims, even) you should achieve something that gives lasting enjoyment to you and your bees.

Features, form and colour

Do not try to fit too many separate features, e.g. rock garden, pool, roses, herbaceous, shrub and annual borders, etc., into a small area. Garden features are highlighted by the spaces left between them, and in most gardens that space is most commonly occupied by lawns. This 'empty' space should be seen as a vital element of design, since it can emphasize bold or striking forms and create vistas.

If you really *must* have all the different

categories of plants in a small area, then create a mixed border. Nothing, to my mind, is more pleasing to the eye than a well-planned combination of different groups of plants. Try to visit gardens open to the public and make a point of looking at their herbaceous and mixed borders. You will pick up a lot of tips of what does and does not work!

Remember that beds of all-deciduous or all-evergreen plants can look really 'flat'. A heather bed, for instance, spotted with dwarf conifers may be fashionable, but it is still boring! The occasional dwarf gorse, deciduous *Berberis* or *Cytisus* look much more natural in a heather bed and would at least give some additional bee forage.

With herbaceous borders, make certain that some of the plants have a persistent form to give some winter interest. Plants such as *Bergenia, Helleborus* and *Kniphofia* are ideal, and why not add the odd shrub such as *Mahonia* or *Cistus*, if space permits?

Form, colour and seasonal interest are important elements that must be considered when designing a garden. To see how an individual border or feature might look when completed, enlarge the scale, for example to 1 in = 3 ft (1 cm = 36 cm), again using plain A3 paper. Draw in horizontal and angled grid lines ⅓ in (8 mm) apart to allow you to make a three-dimensional plan of the area, including background fence or hedge (see Plan 3). Using the information on spacing, height and form given in the plant descriptions, together with the notes in the next section on spacing:

1. Sketch in (*to scale*) the appropriate plant form.

2. Colour in the forms.

3. Note the flowering months and see if all seasons are covered as far as visual interest and bee forage are concerned.

An area of paving and stone walling laid out to
provide a delightful patchwork of colour as well
as enormous interest to bees.

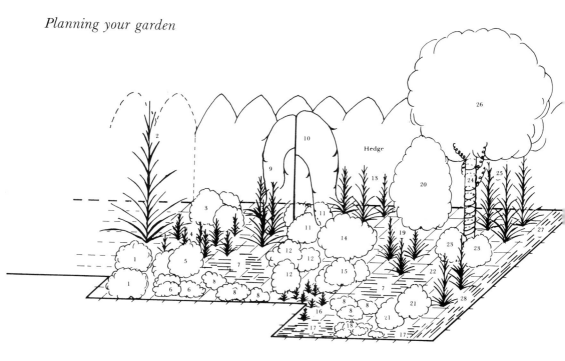

Plan 3. Detailed planting scheme for part of the formal garden design in Plan 1.

1 Viburnum davidii
2 Viburnum x bodnantense 'Dawn'
3 Potentilla fruticosa 'Princess'
4 Lavandula angustifolia
5 Potentilla fruticosa 'Tangerine'
6 Cytisus x beanii
7 Hebe pinguifolia pagei
8 Bergenia 'Evening Glow'
9 Cornus alba 'Spaethii'
10 Buddleia alternifolia
11 Helleborus lividus corsicus
12 Daphne x burkwoodii
13 Hypericum patulum 'Hidcote'
14 Salix lanata
15 Helleborus foetidus
16 Hypericum olympicum
17 Thymus serpyllum 'Doone Valley'
18 Berberis thunbergii 'Atropurpurea Nana'
19 Nepeta gigantea 'Six Hills Hybrid'
20 Philadelphus 'Beauclerk'
21 Cistus x corbariensis
22 Berberis x carminea 'Buccaneer'
23 Skimmia japonica 'Fragrans'
24 Clematis montana 'Rubens'
25 Mahonia x media 'Charity'
26 Acer pseudoplatanus 'Brilliantissimum'
27 Cotoneaster horizontalis
28 Chaenomeles x superba 'Crimson and Gold'

Remember that the constant repetition of any form or colour can become monotonous. Conversely, some repetition is essential to give a sense of unity and to help emphasize particular features.

Do not slavishly plant rows of tall, medium and dwarf plants. Bring forward some of the taller ones, especially those with distinct forms such as *Kniphofia*, *Verbascum* and *Cytisus*, and in this way you will avoid the 'burial mound' effect so commonly seen in many parks and gardens.

Choice of colours in the garden is a personal matter, but all too often the only combinations seen are the 'safe' ones: blues, pinks and yellows with grey, and although there is nothing wrong with this (grey backs up contrasts and softens the impact of strong colours) it would be nice to see a bolder use of colour. How often do we see red and purple or violet, or orange and red juxtaposed? More often in a dress shop than a garden! It really is worth trying, for example, a grouping of the brilliant red *Salvia splendens* with the violet *Verbena venosa* and blue/violet *Heliotrope*. Take care not to have isolated 'spots' amongst other colours; the aim is to create a sense of unity and cohesion throughout.

Spacing

Plant spacing is a contentious subject; most nurserymen and garden designers recommend spacings which, after 2-3 years, will lead to overcrowding. Close spacing in the early years is more visually pleasing and it does help to suppress weed growth. The cost of this is obviously higher than for more open spacing, but for the bulk of private gardens this does not seem to pose a problem. The spacings recommended in this book should enable the plants to cover the ground in 2-3 years.

The suggested spacings for two plants of the *same* genera are given in the plant lists. The planting distance for *Weigela florida*, for example, should be 5 ft (1.5 m). But how do we find a spacing for two plants of widely different 'spreads' such as *Weigela florida* (5 ft/1.5 m) and *Hebe x* 'Carl Teschner' (2 ft/60 cm)? You must halve the spacings for both plants and add the two figures together, i.e. plant them 3½ ft (1.06 m) apart.

Do remember to take account of the ultimate sizes of plants, so that you do not have to restrict them too much by excessive pruning, for this always results in a reduction of the total number of flowers produced.

With slow-growing plants many of us choose either to place them closer together than recommended or plant relatively cheap ground cover between them (such as *Lamium, Thymus, Cotoneaster* and *Polygonum*

affine), and then pull these out at a later date, or allow the chosen plants to smother them.

Trees and shrubs

In your enthusiasm to create a sylvan glade on your 50 x 40 ft (15 x 12 m) garden plot, be sure to choose trees that will not become giants, for your own, your neighbours' and your bees' sakes; remember that there are few plants that thrive in the dense shade beneath such trees, and even fewer that your bees will bother visiting under such circumstances, even if they are in flower. For this reason do not be tempted to plant trees in groups of three or five; settle instead for single specimens, preferably of erect habit, of a size that is in scale with your garden and this will allow you to grow semi-shade-tolerant plants such as *Mahonia* and *Hypericum* right up to the tree bases. No attempt has been made in the plant lists to indicate spacings for trees for this reason.

The same principles as regards scale apply equally to shrubs. There can be few gardens that could, for example, find space for two *Magnolia x soulangeana*.

Unwilling guests

Unless you are prepared to put in a good deal of work on a regular basis year after year (and a surprisingly large number of people are), do not try to grow too many plants unsuitable for your soil conditions. Many people are tempted in this direction when they see rhododendrons and other acid-soil-loving Ericaceous plants in flower. Forget it, and grow lilacs instead, with honeysuckles (for suitable species see *Lonicera* description) growing up and through them.

5 Bee plants: spoilt for choice

There are so many plants that are suitable for the beekeeper's garden that a large estate would be needed to accommodate them all. Several encyclopedias would also be necessary to describe these same plants in sufficient detail for the beekeeper to be able to choose a collection that would also meet his aesthetic requirements!

One man's meat is definitely another man's poison where plants are concerned, and the number of species described within each genus is of necessity rather small, and obviously reflects many personal favourites — for who enjoys growing or describing plants that he does not like?

The average beekeeper's garden is unlikely to be of sufficient size to accommodate large trees or shrubs and so I have concentrated on medium to small plants which, if carefully selected, will in Britain provide pollen and/or nectar from February to November. Bearing in mind that there are nearly always dwarf forms of most genera, even a 'pocket handkerchief garden' can provide this long season of interest for the bees. Few small or even medium-sized gardens can, however, provide sufficient nectar or pollen to significantly contribute to a colony's development, except in the case of early-spring or late-autumn sources of pollen. Many examples of plants providing good pollen at the right time will be found in the text. The beekeeper should, however, try to persuade neighbours, parks departments, hospital groundsmen, or anyone growing flowers within a couple of miles, to grow a number of those mentioned in the text, especially those starred. Success in this effort will make a considerable difference to the well-being of the colonies and the quantity of honey available to the beekeeper at the end of the year. Even giving away a few plants that you do not perhaps have room for in your own garden can be well worth while.

Remember that full sun will encourage bees to work the flowers; plants in shade rarely attract them in any numbers. Bees do not like cold winds either, so some shelter is also desirable. My own garden suffers from a lack of shelter, and as it is a narrow plot there is little I can do: it is very depressing to watch crocus flowers wither and die without ever having been visited by a single bee!

Plants with double flowers have been excluded from the plant lists, since even where the reproductive parts have not been replaced by further rows of petals the frustration of bees attempting to get at the pollen or nectar is obvious. Not having these double-flowered monstrosities in the garden is no loss to me. I cannot think of one double-flowered plant that in any way approaches the beauty and simplicity of a single-flowered one, whether it be rose, chestnut or tulip.

Kitchen Garden

Most of this book will deal with the flower and, to a lesser extent, fruit garden, this being the place where plants of interest to the honey bee will mainly be found. Of plants grown in the kitchen garden only those which are grown for seed, or for the fruit (e.g. marrow), are of interest to bees, and these amount to only two or three plants. Both the broad bean, *Vicia faba*, and the scarlet runner bean, *Phaseolus coccineus*, supply both nectar and pollen for the bees, and need to attract them as they require bee pollination, the latter needing it to set seed. Where commercial crops of either of these plants are grown, colonies of honey bees are often hired in to provide good pollination and so enhance profitability of the crop.

V. faba is unique in that honey bees work it in three different ways. Pollen collectors and some nectar gatherers go in from the front of the flower and it is these which effect pollination. Short-tongued bumble-bees, *Bombus* species, cut a hole in the base of the flower to get at the nectar and, after this has been done, honey bees work through the holes as well. Finally, the honey bees work the black spot on the stipules, which is an extra-floral nectary and at times produces a nectar which is higher in sugar content than that in the flower itself. It is often possible to see all three methods of work occurring at one time. The resulting honey is rich in flavour and medium in colour. The tips of the later spring sowings are commonly plastered with blackfly, *Aphis fabae*, during July and

A bee stealing nectar through the hole cut by bumble bees in a broad bean flower. Similar holes are visible on other flowers. At top right the black spot on the triangular stipule marks the extra-floral nectary.

August. To avoid having to spray, nip out the tips of the plants either at the first sign of attack or once four tiers of pods have formed.

Phaseolus coccineus has an extremely complex flower and therefore needs a sophisticated pollinating insect, such as a bee, to effect entry and bring about the pollination without which only a very tiny amount of seed is set and pods retained. *P. vulgaris*, the French bean, has white flowers which are self-pollinating and are of no interest to the bee. Similarly the garden pea, *Pisum sativum*, provides neither nectar nor pollen and is completely self-pollinating.

The only other plants normally found in the kitchen garden which are of interest to bees are the gourds such as vegetable marrow, ridge cucumbers and gherkins. These provide nectar and pollen in quantity, but the number of flowers per plant is so small that they are not always searched out by the bees. Should the gardener allow brassicas to remain in the soil and flower, the bees will be really pleased, as they are very attractive and provide good quantities of both pollen and nectar.

The abbreviations and symbols that now follow are intended to provide a rapid reference as to the suitability of plants for given situations. The number of plant forms/shapes has been kept to an absolute minimum for simplicity's sake, but there are obviously many gradations between them.

Abbreviations and symbols used in plant descriptions

Nec/Pol	— nectar and/or pollen source
*	— particularly good bee plants
H.	— herbaceous
Shr.	— shrub
T.	— tree
B/C.	— bulb or corm
Ann.	— annual
A(h).	— hardy annual
Bien.	— biennial
🌿	— evergreen
🌱	— deciduous
🌾	— erect growth
🌿	— horizontal growth
☁	— rounded outline
🌿	— climber
🌳	— weeping habit
🍒	— attractive fruit or berries
ht:	— height in feet/inches and metric (italic)
dist:	— spacing between plants of same species in feet/inches and metric (italic). See also note on page 35.

Jul-Sep	— flowering months
acid	— requires acid soil
alk	— requires alkaline soil
wet	— requires damp situation
dry	— requires dry situation
salt tol	— tolerant of salt spray (seaside conditions)

full sun	— optimum situation
semi-shade	
shade	

Plant descriptions

Abelia Nec/Pol Shr. ◯
ht: 4 ft *1.25 m* dist: 3 ft *1 m*
full sun

Abelia is a real charmer, with its clusters of bell-shaped five-petalled flowers so profusely borne over several months, making it a very valuable garden and bee plant. The brown or pink sepals are showy in their own right and are very persistent, remaining long after the flowers have fallen and especially attractive when viewed against the dark evergreen or semi-evergreen leaves.

Abelias are very easy to grow, even on heavy soils, as long as the drainage is good. Their one weakness is that they are not entirely hardy, and most species require the shelter of a wall or other plants; this is not easily achieved, since they must also have full sun. Common winter damage amounts to branches being killed back, but these will usually sprout again from near their bases, if one is patient. I say patient because the first new shoots may not appear until June, in common with many other severely frost-damaged plants. One wonders how many poor plants have been 'ripped untimely' from their beds by impatient gardeners who have not even suspected their plant's struggle for survival! Cuttings taken in August root very easily, and these really can be your insurance policy against a really hard winter.

A. chinensis Jul-Aug, ⅄ The fragrant flowers are white with a rose flush, sepals pink.

'Edward Goucher' Jul-Sep, ⅊⅊ This semi-evergreen cultivar has purplish-pink flowers.

A. schumanii May-Aug, ⅄ Flowers rose-pink, up to 1 inch (2.5 cm) long.

Acer (Maples) Nec/Pol ⅄ ◯
full sun, semi-shade

There is a large number of species and an increasing number of cultivars in this variable and decorative genus of deciduous trees and shrubs. Some attain heights of over 100 ft (30 m), whilst others may reach only 6-8 ft (2-2.5 m). Fortunately some of the larger types are frequently found in the wild, where their free-flowering characteristics ensure a good 'crop' of early nectar and pollen. The nectar is secreted by a fleshy green disc, to which the stamens are attached. If the eight greenish-yellow, spreading petals are removed, the whole structure looks rather like an eight-legged stool. The double-winged seeds, or 'helicopters' as they are known, are familiar to all and are freely produced by most species.

Most acers are grown for their bark, leaf shape or autumn colour, but the flowers are very showy in some species. The leaves are typically palmate, as in the maple leaf emblem of Canada, but they may have three or as many as five lobes, depending on species.

A. campestre (Hedge or Field Maple) T. ht: 20-40 ft *6-12 m* Apr. Occasionally up to 70 ft (21 m), this tree is more usually 15-20 ft (4.5-6 m), and frequently seen, as the common name implies, in hedges. It has the typical palmate leaf, up to 4 in (10 cm) across, and small green flowers held erect at first, and then pendulous. In autumn the leaves turn a clear golden yellow. A beautiful tree if you have the space; if not, you could perhaps plant one in a local hedgerow!

A. capillipes T. ht: 30 ft *9 m* May. A rather small tree whose green bark has attractive white striations. The flowers are yellow and the new growth is an attractive coral red. The species *pensylvanicum* is similar and is more suitable for slightly acid soils.

A. griseum (Paperback Maple) T. ht: 25 ft *7.5 m* May. One of the most beautiful of all garden trees, with bark that flakes away to reveal the varied coppery brown coloration beneath. The three-lobed leaves often turn a beautiful red or scarlet in autumn. Flowers pendulous.

A. negundo (Box Elder) T. ht: 45 ft *13.5 m* May. A rather fast growing tree, with bright green young shoots and leaves with 3-5 leaflets. Most frequently seen in its much less vigorous form 'Elegans', which has showy yellow marginal leaf variegation. The male and female flowers are borne on separate plants, so try if possible to obtain a male, since the females bear no pollen.

A. palmatum (Japanese Maple) Shr. ht: 30 ft *9 m* dist: 10 ft *3 m* May-Jun, acid. Japanese maples will grow to 20-30 ft (6-9 m) if well protected by other trees, but they are more usually seen as smaller, relatively slow growing shrubs, some 4-15 ft (1.25-4.5 m) in height. They are beautiful and elegant plants even in winter, when the dense twiggy growth can be seen to best effect.

The leaves, which turn to brilliant reds and oranges in autumn, have 5-7 toothed lobes. The cultivar 'Heptalobum Osakazuki' is my own particular favourite, with its incredible mixture of fiery red and orange autumn leaf coloration. It is, however, not freely available in many garden centres, but there are many other good cultivars.

Shelter from wind, particularly in spring, is essential if the new growth of all the *palmatum* cultivars is not to be badly scorched.

'Atropurpureum' Shr. ht: 6-15 ft *2-4.5 m* dist: 6-8 ft *2-2.5 m* Certainly the most frequently grown cultivar and deservedly so, with its bronze-crimson leaf coloration.

'Dissectum' Shr. ht: 4 ft *1.25 m* dist: 4 ft *1.25 m* Much less vigorous than most of the other cultivars in this genus, this has attractive much-divided toothed leaves.

There are several other cultivars with purple, yellow and even variegated foliage. All are first-class garden plants in a sheltered spot with acid soil.

A. platanoides T. ht: 70 ft *21 m* Apr. The Norway maple, with its erect clusters of bright yellow-green flowers, is a familiar sight in Europe's April hedgerows, and although the individual flowers are small they are present in sufficient numbers to create quite an impact, especially when seen cheek by jowl with blackthorn. Unless you have an estate or very large garden, then this species, with its wonderful buttercup-yellow autumn coloration, is best admired in a natural woodland setting. Choose instead one of a number of excellent cultivars, slower growing but ultimately still very large trees, which have found their way into many gardens.

'Erectum' ht: 20-30 ft *6-9 m* Its erect habit and slower growth make this a most suitable cultivar for the garden.

'Crimson King' ht: 40 ft *12 m* Dark purple leaves and similarly coloured seeds.

'Schwedleri' ht: 40 ft *12 m* The leaves and young growth are a rich crimson-purple, paler beneath and very handsome towards the end of the flowering period.

A. pseudoplatanus (Sycamore) T. ht: 80 ft *24 m* May. A very common tree throughout the British Isles and woodland mountainous areas of Europe (and present even in very exposed areas), often in sufficient numbers for it to be a considerable source of nectar on warm early summer days. Again, like the Norway maple, do not contemplate planting this giant in your own garden, but choose instead one of the excellent slow-growing cultivars.

'Brilliantissimum' ht: 15 ft *4.5 m* Rather slow growing and mop-headed, this is without doubt one of the very best small trees. The new spring growth is a gorgeous soft pink streaked with lime green, against which the large clusters of pendulous yellow-green flowers can be viewed. Unfortunately, the leaves turn a rather more mundane green as the summer progresses.

'Prinz Handjery' ht: 20 ft *6 m* Rather similar to 'Brilliantissimum', but with leaves purple-tinged beneath.

Achillea (Yarrow) Nec. H.

full sun

Given good drainage and a sunny position there are few plants that will reward you and your bees with more flowers for such little effort.

The individual 'flowers' (broad ray-florets variable in number) are about ¼ inch (6 mm) diameter, but there is usually a very large number of them forming each flat-topped head, and a good number of the stiffly erect flower stems to each plant.

Most of the species are clump-forming and the long, deeply bisected basal leaves (rather like hairy fern fronds) usually come through the winter unscathed. The leaves are in fact pungent and I rank them in the same 'group' as lavender in this respect; very pleasant.

The flowering stems and flower heads dry well (except possibly for *millefolium* cultivars).

A. ageratifolia ht: 6 in *15 cm* dist: 9 in *23 cm* Jun-Jul. Leaves silvery, white flower heads.

A. filipendulina 'Gold Plate' ht: 4 ft *1.2 m* dist: 2-2½ ft *60-73 cm* Jun-Aug. Large golden-yellow flower heads.

'Coronation Gold' ht: 3 ft *91 cm* dist: 2 ft *60 cm* Jun-Aug. Similar to 'Gold Plate'.

'Moonshine' ht: 2 ft *60 cm* dist: 18 in *45 cm* Jun-Aug. A beautiful cultivar with feathery silver foliage and bright yellow flowers.

A. millefolium 'Cerise Queen' ht: 2½ ft *75 cm* dist: 18 in *45 cm* May-Sep. Loose heads of cerise-red flowers.

'Lilac Beauty' ht: 2 ft *30 cm* dist: 18 in *45 cm* May-Sep. Lilac flowers.

A. serrata 'W.B. Child' ht: 2 ft *30 cm* dist: 18 in *45 cm* Jun and Sep. Large, white, loose flower heads.

A. tomentosa ht: 6 in *15 cm* dist: 9 in *23 cm* Jun-Aug. Very 'woolly' foliage and deep yellow flower heads.

Achilleas spread quickly and friends are usually only too willing to give pieces away in an attempt to control their expansionist habits.

Aesculus Nec/Pol
full sun

There are few trees that can rival the magnificence of an eighty-foot horse-chestnut in full flower. There are, however, some *Aesculus* of less massive proportions with equally beautiful flowers. All produce nectar freely and are enthusiastically worked by bees, as is obvious from the brick-red pollen loads being taken into the hive. Care should be taken in the selection of the species planted, as the red horse-chestnut *A. x carnea* does at times poison bees working it. Bumble bees are more readily affected, but often the ground under the tree will be littered with bees unable to fly. The bees are often attacked by birds, and will be seen to have lost the ends of their abdomens.

The large flowers, or candles as they are commonly known, are broadly pyramidal in shape and are made up of many individual florets, the corollas of which have four or five unequal flared petals and protruding, upwardly-curved stamens. The large, five-to-seven-lobed leaves are coarsely toothed, distinct and handsome.

The large sticky buds of the horse-chestnut are conspicuous and attractive, as are the green spiny cases that hold the conkers, which usually fall after a few sharp frosts. A conker fresh from its husk is a most beautiful thing, so shiny as to be reflective, and looking good enough to eat, which it is not!

All *Aesculus* colour well in the autumn, usually in the gold and russet colour range.

A. hippocastanum (Horse-chestnut) T. ht: 80 ft *24 m* May. Far too large for most gardens, so hope your neighbours will have it, for you and the bees to enjoy. The white, mostly male flowers are about 12 in (30 cm) long, with yellow spots, and turn pink as they age.

A. parviflora Shr. ht: 8 ft *2.5 m* dist: 8-9 ft *2.5-2.75 m* Jul-Aug. White flowers with red anthers and, like *pavia* below, really grown as a shrub.

A. pavia (Red Buckeye) ht: 10 ft *3 m* dist: 10 ft *3 m* Jun-Jul. Crimson flowers up to 6 in (15 cm) long.

Alcea syn. Althaea (Hollyhock) Nec/Pol H.
ht: 6-8 ft *2-2.5 m* dist: 2-3 ft *60-90 cm*
Jul-Sep, full sun

This is a real cottage garden plant, with tall elegant flower spikes, now all too infrequently seen, particularly in its most interesting and attractive single form. The large five-petalled, saucer-like flowers are very showy and have a satin-like sheen. The basal flowers open first, and the large club-like mass of stamens are typical of the Malvaceae family and bear masses of very large pollen grains. The bees work it mainly for the pollen, especially useful late in the season, and bees can be seen returning to the hive covered with it, sometimes with a distinct white mark on their backs in a place they do not seem able to reach to clean.

The leaves are generally grey-green and quite rough-textured.

A. ficifolia A variable species with white, yellow or orange flowers up to 4 in (10 cm) in diameter, and deeply lobed leaves. Biennial or short-lived perennial.

A. rosea Available in a mixture of colours — pink, crimson, rose, cream and white; the leaves are broadly heart-shaped.

'Nigra' ht: 6 ft *2 m* A dull red-black, too sombre for my taste.

Be warned that most, if not all, hollyhocks sold by garden centres will be doubles, so you may need to raise your own from seed sown outdoors in spring; the resultant plants will normally flower in the following spring. Plant them into their final positions as soon as possible, since they are reputed not to like root disturbance, but I have to say this has not been my experience.

Alchemilla (Lady's Mantle) Nec/Pol H. ☁
Jun-Sep, full sun, semi-shade

The delicacy of the leaves, and especially the flowers, belies the tough adaptability of this superb tufted plant which thrives in sun, shade or wet and dry soils alike. The individual flowers are small, yellow or yellow-green and borne in great numbers in clusters (similar to *Gypsophila* but not quite as loose), held well above the rounded and serrated leaves. A most attractive and easily grown plant. I have one particularly good specimen, collected in the wild and un-named (not for want of trying), no more than 2 in (5 cm) high with very small leaves borne on the most beautiful thin wiry red stems. As with all alchemillas, the papery brown stipules are a distinctive feature.

You are very unlikely to find more than two species on sale in most garden centres, for I fear *Alchemilla* is just too delicate-looking for most people's tastes; but every bold and 'vulgar' plant needs its counterpoint and for this it is perfect, and it is much loved by flower-arrangers!

All species tend to seed freely and become invasive, so remove the old flower heads to avoid being taken over.

A. alpina (Alpine Lady's Mantle) ht: 8 in *20 cm* dist: 18 in *45 cm* Do not be fooled by its name into thinking this is not a vigorous and even rampant grower — it is. The flowers are more green than yellow, and are borne in dense clusters; leaves are silvery beneath and their margins are silkily hairy.

A. mollis ht: 18 in *45 cm* dist: 18-24 in *45-60 cm* A rather taller-growing species with larger, pale green, softly hairy leaves.

Allium Nec/Pol B/C. ⚘
full sun, shade

Even if you do not like the culinary types — leeks, garlic, chives and, of course, the common onion — you will be captivated by the more ornamental forms, which have a wide colour range and vary from the small rounded flower heads of *A. flavum* to the more massive heads of *A. christophii*. The individual flowers which make up the flower heads are star-like, with six narrow, shallowly spoon-shaped petals around the six stamens and a single stigma above the ovary. This is circular at first, but swells into a 3-5 lobed 'cluster' once the seed starts to form, making these forms very attractive as dried flowers.

The leaves are normally long and narrow, but may be tubular, triangular or flat in section. In the common wild ramson (*A. ursinum*) the leaves are oval with very long stalks, whilst the leaves of *A. christophii* are lance-shaped and stalkless.

A variable genus then, but well worth growing. Try not to trample on the plants or crush them in any way or you will carry the smell around with you for some time! (Fortunately neither the honey nor the dried flower heads carry the typical onion aroma.) Most species are worked for nectar, and onion honey is produced in California and elsewhere where the crops are grown for seed.

A. flatuense ht: 3 ft *1 m* dist: 9 in *23 cm* Jun-Jul. Tennis-ball size flower heads of pale lilac, leaves blue-green and broadly strap-shaped.

A. cernuum ht: 1 ft *30 cm* dist: 6 in *15 cm* Jun-Jul. Nodding heads of deep pink flowers.

A. christophii syn. *albopilosum* ht: 2 ft *60 cm* dist: 9

in *23 cm* Jun-Jul. Massive flower heads of pale purple with a metallic sheen.

A. flavum ht: 9 in *23 cm* dist: 6 in *15 cm* Jul-Aug. Yellow bell-shaped flowers carried on small heads above blue-grey foliage.

A. moly ht: 1 ft *30 cm* dist: 6 in *15 cm* Jun-Jul. Bright yellow flower heads 3 inches (7 cm) or so across, and grey-green leaves. A handsome but vigorous plant that should be given the company of other 'invaders' to help keep it in check — try *Nepeta* or some of the mat-forming thymes.

A. narcissiflorum ht: 8 in *20 cm* dist: 4 in *10 cm* Jun-Jul. A charming dwarf species with nodding pink flowers.

A. oreophilum ostrowskianum ht: 8 in *20 cm* dist: 6 in *15 cm* Jun-Jul. Deep rose-pink flower heads up to 4 in (10 cm) across.

A. schoenoprasum (Chives) ht: 9-18 in *23-45 cm* dist: 1-2 ft *30-60 cm* Jun-Aug. A very underrated and highly decorative plant with cylindrical leaves and tight clusters of mauve flowers. It deserves to be much more widely grown as an ornamental plant in its own right, and is avidly worked for nectar and pollen by bees. There is enormous variation between the various strains of this species. My own plants are a mere 9 in (23 cm) high, whilst 18 in (46 cm) is not an uncommon height.

A. tuberosum ht: 18 in *45 cm* dist: 1 ft *30 cm* Sept-Oct. A white-flowered species.

Alstroemeria (Peruvian Lily) H. Nec/Pol

ht: 3-4 ft *1-1.25 m* dist: 28-30 in *70-75 cm* Jun-Aug, full sun
The masses of six-pointed trumpet-like flowers, 2½-3½ in (6-9 cm) in diameter, are borne in clusters at the top of erect leafy stems, and with their satin-like sheen are quite beautiful. The inner petals are often gorgeously veined, splotched and suffused with a contrasting colour. What an inspiration these flowers would be for a fabric designer! They are certainly popular, and deservedly so, and supplies are available for a good part of the year from the commercial glasshouse industry.

The tuberous root system is easily damaged, so always buy container-grown specimens. As with many plants with fleshy roots, drainage must be good if rotting-off losses are to be avoided. Also, unless you live in a mild district, try to ensure that you choose one of the hardier types listed below.

A. aurantiaca 'Dover Orange' Orange-red flowers.

'Ligtu hybrids' A really superb mixture of shades of pink to golden-orange to orange-red. These slightly more vigorous hybrids are now far more commonly available than any of the older species or cultivars.

Alyssum saxatile (Golden Alyssum) Nec/Pol

ht: 9 in *23 cm* dist: 12-18 in *30-45 cm* Apr-Jun, dry, full sun
The bright yellow flowers are a rather harsh colour, but April can be a pretty dull time for the garden and bees alike, and the masses of these small cruciferous flowers, completely obscuring the small grey leaves, are a definite tonic to both. It is strong enough to thrive amongst small shrubs and herbaceous plants, as long as it has good drainage and full sun. For the rock garden, choose the cultivar 'Compactum', which is less invasive. The soft lemon-yellow flowers of 'Citrinum' are less harsh than those of *A. saxatile*.

Trimming over the faded flower stems encourages bushiness and prolongs the life of the plants.

Amelanchier (Snowy Mespilus, June Berry) Nec/Pol Shr. T.

ht: 10-12 ft *3-3.5 m* dist: 12-15 ft *3.5-4.5 m* Apr, full sun, semi-shade
Few plants can have as many attributes as this easily grown, large, deciduous shrub or small tree. It is said to prefer relatively lime-free soils, but some of the best specimens I have seen showed no symptoms of disliking a soil with a pH in excess of 7.00 (although the autumn colour was certainly not as good).

In spring, the twiggy shoots are blanketed with erect clusters of snowy flowers. Each flower may be 1-1½ in (2.5-3.5 cm) in diameter, with five, rather narrow, strap-shaped petals.

43

The young leaves at this time are a coppery brown and provide an unusual and pleasant contrast with the flowers. The flowers may be followed by red or black fruits in the autumn, but these quickly succumb to the attention of birds, and are certainly not a prominent feature.

The leaves, however, are prominent and can provide breathtaking red-orange, orange-green, yellow-red combinations of colour — even on the same branch. Definitely one of the top five plants for autumn colour. No largish garden should be without its *Amelanchier*; not least because it must be one of the earliest sources of pollen. The genus is well represented in North America by some nine species, all of which are thought to be reasonably productive honey plants.

A. lamarkii This is by far the most commonly grown species, although you might not think so if you are hunting through the average nursery for a specimen — in the past it has been widely but incorrectly known as *canadensis*, and old habits die hard. Other names frequently applied to it include *laevis* and *x grandiflora*. If you buy any of these you will in all probability end up with *lamarkii*! The leaves of this species are large, up to 4 in (10 cm) long by 2 in (5 cm) wide, and finely toothed. It has red berries.

I have a large 12 x 12 ft (3.5 x 3.5 m) specimen growing next to a dark green Lawson's Cypress, and the contrast in spring and again in autumn is beautiful.

'Rubescens' Flowers tinted pink.

Anchusa Nec.
full sun

The flowers of all the species and cultivars listed are brilliant gentian-blue and have five rounded petals, very slightly cupped, with a small white eye fringed with short hairs that protect the nectar from rain and short-tongued insects, but not from the honey bee. The leaves are narrow and very rough to the touch. Not the same colour as a cat's tongue, but much the same feel!

A. azurea 'Loddon Royalist' H. ht: 3 ft *1 m* dist: 2 ft *60 cm* Jun-Sep. A fabulous plant with a long much-branched flower spike, all parts of which are bristly and rough to the touch.

The root systems of the perennial types are very fleshy and easily damaged, so try to buy container-grown plants; and if you have to move them do so straight after flowering, while the soil is still warm, so that damaged parts heal quickly.

'Morning Glory' H. ht: 4-5 ft *1.25-1.5 m* dist: 2½-3 ft *75-90 cm* Jun-Sep. Deeper blue flowers.

A. capensis 'Blue Angel' A(h). ht: 9 in *23 cm* dist: 9 in *23 cm* Jun-Nov. A less elegant form than its taller relatives, but with just as many flowers.

'Blue Bird' A(h). ht: 12 in *30 cm* dist: 9 in *23 cm* Jun-Nov. Just a bit larger than 'Blue Angel'. There are now pink cultivars available.

A. officinalis (alkanet) A wild flower but well established in some gardens, it is a joy to all bees and many other insects. Flowering throughout the summer, it continues to provide both nectar and pollen at times when there is little else about.

Anemone (Windflower) Pol.
full sun, semi-shade

There is far more to this interesting genus of largely bulbous or rhizomatous plants than is to be seen in the florist's window. There are many European species, some dwarf, and some of the very best of all herbaceous plants in *A. x hybrida* and its cultivars.

Anemones are easily grown, and the bulk of them flower from early to late spring, providing large amounts of pollen at a time when few other sources may be available. Anemones have no nectaries. The flowers, which are normally carried singly, have a whorl of three leaves some way beneath them, parsley-like and attractive (in most species) long after the flowers are over.

A. blanda B/C. ht: 4 in *10 cm* dist: 3-4 in *7.5-10 cm* Mar-Apr. The species has 1½-2 in (3.5-5 cm) white-eyed, star-like, pale blue flowers, but there are also cultivars with pink, red and purple flowers. Best planted in August or September, 3-4 in (7.5-10 cm) deep.

Anemone apenina, a very versatile small plant.

A. apenina B/C. ht: 5 in *12.5 cm* dist: 3-4 in *7.5-10 cm* Mar-May. Very similar to *blanda*, but longer flowering and also ideal for naturalizing in short grass. Both are charming dwarf plants for the rock garden, or at the front of a tree, shrub or herbaceous border.

A. coronaria (Poppy Anemone) B/C. ht: 10-12 in *25-30 cm* dist: 3-4 in *7.5-10 cm* Mar-Oct. This is one of the parents from which the florists' strains such as 'St Brigid' and 'De Caen' were bred. There are now several named cultivars of these available in a wide range of bold gaudy colours. The petals are rounded and only eight in number, as compared to, say, *blanda*, which may have up to twenty. The pollen is a slatey blue-grey colour. They are not reliably hardy, so unless you are prepared to protect your plants with cloches (and this is quite commonly done for autumn-planted tubers), plant only in late spring and summer to give a succession of flowers throughout mid-summer and autumn. Plant the tubers 2 in (5 cm) deep.

A. x hybrida H. ⚘ Aug-Nov. The nomenclature of this superb late-flowering group of herbaceous plants is much confused, at least as far as the poor gardener is concerned, for whilst *x hybrida* is the name now officially used the plants are still frequently sold under their original species names: *hupehensis* and *japonica*, or even a combination of both: *hupehensis japonica*. The name *x hybrida* is in fact now given to crosses between the two species! Be all this as it may, the 2½-3 in (6.5-7.5 cm) flowers, with their rounded satiny petals, are quite exquisite in form and texture. They are not carried singly as in other species, but in erect long-flowering compound heads that display buds and flowers beautifully. All have large central bosses of yellow-tipped stamens. The leaves are also bold, trifoliate with unequal lobes — with nothing parsley-like about them.

There are several double and semi-double cultivars, so do make sure you buy what you want.

'Bressingham Glow' ht: 2 ft *60 cm* dist: 18 in *45 cm* Deep pink flowers.

'Honorine Jobert' ht: 4 ft *1.25 m* dist: 2-3 ft *60-90 cm* Pure white flowers.

'Kriemhilde' ht: 3 ft *90 cm* dist: 2 ft *60 cm* Rose-pink flowers. I have this cultivar in the herbaceous border, where it looks very showy against holly, but any other dark background would do as well.

A. nemerosa (Wood Anemone) ht: 4 in *10 cm* dist: 3-4 in *7.5-10 cm* Mar-May. The charming wood anemone, with its pink-flushed, white or pale blue, star-like, nodding flowers, has very catholic tastes regarding soil and site. In my garden they grow wild in short grass on the banks of a burn, and I have not the heart to add any of the deep blue or lavender-coloured cultivars to them.

However, in spite of its innocent looks, this is a very poisonous plant (not to bees), and its sap will also cause skin blistering.

Unlike *x hybrida*, which is fibrous rooted, and the other species listed which are tuberous, *nemerosa* is rhizomatous. Take care to plant new rhizomes quickly (to prevent drying out) to a depth of 2 in (5 cm).

Anthemis Nec/Pol H. 🐝🌿
Jun-Sep

Just one of the enormous family of plants with composite flowers, like daisies and dandelions, which all bees find so attractive and rewarding. The leaves of all species are rather feathery and much divided, with a typical chamomile-like fragrance when crushed. This combination of leaves and flowers makes a rather handsome plant.

A. cupaniana 〓 ht: 6 in *15 cm* dist: 2-3 ft *60-90 cm* full sun, semi-shade. Forms great spreading mats of silver foliage topped with 2 in (5 cm) white flowers with a yellow eye. An ideal plant for a dry area where space is not at a premium.

A. sancti-johannis 🌼 ht: 18 in *45 cm* dist: 12-18 in *30-45 cm* full sun. Flowers of bright orange, leaves hairy and grey.

A. tinctoria x 'Grallagh Gold' (Ox-eye Chamomile) 🌼 ht: 2½ ft *75 cm* dist: 2 ft *60 cm* full sun. Somewhat deeper orange than *sancti-johannis*.

'Wargrave' Pale lemon-yellow flowers.

Arabis Nec/Pol 🐝🌿 〓
full sun, semi-shade

Mostly rather dwarf tufted or mat-forming perennials with basal rosettes of oval or lance-shaped leaves. The short flowering stems, which also bear leaves, are topped with clusters of rounded or flat-topped flowers, which may be white or even deep red-purple, depending on the cultivar. Like most crucifers, this plant provides nectar and pollen and is very attractive to the honey bee. As it flowers so early in the season it is a very useful plant in the spring build-up of honey bee colonies. The four petals are divided to the base, and are 'held' in place by the sepals. Nectar collects in copious amounts at the base of the sepals and petals.

A. albida 'Rosabella' ht: 4 in *10 cm* dist: 9 in *23 cm* Mar-Jun. Fragrant pale pink flowers, leaves grey-green.

'Coccinea' ht: 4 in *10 cm* Flowers a deeper red.

A. blepharophylla 'Spring Charm' ht: 4 in *10 cm* dist: 9 in *23 cm* Mar-Jun. Very showy fragrant and intense carmine flowers very nearly 1 inch (2.5 cm) across; leaves green, somewhat rough. The sepals are distinctly boat-shaped and take on a good deal of the flower coloration. Although a native of California, this species is in my experience completely hardy in cooler areas such as Britain. Try it for a change in your spring bedding display instead of or with *Bellis* or *Myosotis*.

A. ferdinandi-coburgii 'Variegata' ht: 5 in *12.5 cm* dist: 12-15 in *30-45 cm* Apr-Jun. A really awful name for a first-class rock garden or edging plant. The small flowers are white, as are the sepals, with occasional green markings. The bluntly pointed leaves are up to 1½ in (4 cm) long, with wide irregular marginal variegation which often turns deep pink in winter.

Runners are freely produced and root easily on contact with the soil.

An excellent ground-cover plant that associates well with spring flowering bulbs such as *Chionodoxa*, *Muscari* and *Scilla*.

Armeria (Thrift, Sea Pink) Nec/Pol 🐝🌿 🌼
salt tol, full sun

Seen growing wild in coastal or mountain areas, the tight hummocks of dark green grass-like foliage of the thrifts could easily be mistaken for the sheep-mown grass with which they so happily combine. But when in flower there is no mistaking this superb little plant with its iron constitution.

The tight clusters of flower buds appear in spring. The flower stalks quickly elongate and the small, five-petalled, tubular flowers open, forming a dense, almost spherical, head of flowers. The bees visit the flowers in great numbers, and since there can be several hundred individual flowers in just one square foot the 'grazing' is good.

A. juniperfolia syn. *cespitosa* ht: 3 in *7.5 cm* dist: 6 in *15 cm* Apr-May. Where space is really restricted, or you have a genuine rock garden or scree bed, one of the several cultivars of this tight pincushion-like plant with its almost stalkless flowers is ideal. The cultivar 'Bevans' has deep rose flowers, whilst 'Deep Form' has pale pink flowers and the tightest growth habit of the whole genus.

A. maritima ht: 8 in *20 cm* dist: 9 in *23 cm* May-Jul. The flower heads are almost 1 in (2.5 cm) across. The cultivar 'Alba' has white flowers, whilst 'Vindictive' is deep pink.

Aster Nec/Pol H. 🌲
full sun

The name aster comes from the Greek word for star, and this is an apt description of the flowers, particularly the single-flowered cultivars in which we are most interested, although even the doubles open up eventually to give access to the bees. Most members of the daisy family are highly attractive to bees, and provide nectar and pollen in good quantity. The late-flowering Michaelmas daisies have the added advantage of coming into flower when there is very little bee forage, and colonies are needing to collect fresh pollen to add to their winter store of protein. Not only is pollen stored in the cells at this time of year, but the bees are also storing protein within their bodies, in an organ called the fatbody, and this helps them survive the winter and reduces the ill effects of some diseases, such as nosema, a protozoan gut parasite. To the honey bee, any income of fresh food in autumn is very valuable, and the beekeeper-gardener should remember this when planning his garden.

Asters are a large and varied genus of plants perhaps characterized best by the Michaelmas daisies, known to most gardeners for their lax growth habits, late flowers and susceptibility to mildew; a reputation largely undeserved if a careful selection is made. There are also some beautiful dwarf spring/summer-flowering species and cultivars, and these are very suitable for the rock garden.

A. alpinus ht: 6-9 in *15-23 cm* dist: 6-9 in *15-23 cm* May-Jul. There can be few greater pleasures for the gardener than collecting seed in the wild, raising the plants and awaiting with eager anticipation the first flowers. My own plants were raised from seed collected on a walking holiday in the Maritime Alps, and they never cease to bring me great pleasure when the first lilac-blue flowers open in spring. The single flowers are 1½-2 in (4-5 cm) across, and their large flat yellow centres are packed with florets.

The leaves are mostly basal and spoon-shaped. White and pink forms are frequently to be seen in gardens — as indeed they are in the wild.

A. tongolensis 'Napsbury' ht: 9 in *23 cm* dist: 9 in *23 cm* Jun-Jul. A mat-forming cultivar with purple-blue flowers with orange centres. Often seen in cultivation as *yunnanensis* 'Napsbury'.

Michaelmas daisies are, strictly speaking, cultivars of the *novae-belgii* group, but all the species and cultivars described below also commonly bear this name. The flowers are borne in erect terminal clusters varying in size from 1½-3 in (4-8 cm), and the leaves are narrow in relation to their length.

Many of the older types were tall and prone to collapse at around flowering time, making staking an essential operation. The newer introductions have often been selected for their more dwarf characteristics, making them easier to manage; so, unless you enjoy staking and tying, or really want tall plants, choose from the new types listed here.

A. amellus 'Brilliant' ht: 2 ft *60 cm* dist: 1½-2 ft *45-60 cm* Aug-Oct. Large bright pink flowers.

'Violet Queen' ht: 2 ft *60 cm*.dist: 1½-2 ft *45-60 cm* Aug-Oct. Violet flowers.

A. dumosus 'Lady in Blue' ht: 12 in *30 cm* dist: 12 in *30 cm* Sep-Oct. Semi-double lavender-blue flowers. Susceptible to mildew.

A. x frikartii 'Monch' ht: 2-2½ ft *60-75 cm* dist: 1½-2 ft *45-60 cm* Jul-Oct. Large 2 in (5 cm) rich lavender-blue flowers, centre yellow-orange.

A. novae-belgii ht: 1 ft *30 cm* dist: 9-12 in *23-30 cm* Sep-Oct. All cultivars are susceptible to mildew.

'Little Pink Beauty' Semi-double flowers.

'Snowsprite' Both this and the cultivar above have flowers which contrast well with the very dark green foliage.

A. sedifolius nanus syn. *acris* ht: 2 ft *60 cm* dist: 18 in *45 cm* Sep-Oct. Masses of small violet-blue flowers with few petals. Leaves small and pale green, smelling of carrot when bruised.

A. thomsonii nana ht: 12 in *30 cm* dist: 12 in *30 cm* Jul-Oct. Pale blue flowers.

Some taller-growing cultivars that would help to extend the colour range are: *novae angliae* 'Alma Potschke' Cerise, semi-double, and 'Harrington's Pink' Salmon; *novae belgii* 'Ernest Ballard' Crimson.

* **Aubrieta** (Aubretia) Nec/Pol 🌱 H. ≢
ht: 6 in *15 cm* dist: 1½-2 ft *45-60 cm*
Mar-May, full sun, semi-shade

A single plant will, over two or three years, cover a square yard (metre) of soil or cascade over a similar area of wall, and when smothered with its small blue, purple or white flowers it would be difficult to imagine a more pleasing sight. The plants are usually only a few inches high, but will 'clamber up' to a height of 2 ft (60 cm) or so if taller plants nearby provide competition. They are equally at home in sunny south-facing crevices on walls or rock gardens with virtually no soil or moisture and a high pH, as they are in richer soils with a low pH and a northerly aspect. The foliage is an unremarkable grey-green. The bees will, of course, prefer those plants in full sun. They will, however, work the flowers at any time when the air temperature is high enough to make flight possible, because *Aubrieta* is another member of the crucifer family, and thus very attractive to honey bees.

As soon as the flowers are over, clip off the old flower stalks with shears. This prevents the plants looking untidy and encourages new growth from the base of the plant. Cuttings taken from these new shoots will root easily in May or June.

The matted habit of *Aubrieta* encourages slugs and snails, and although the plants do not appear to suffer damage themselves, they do provide bases for attacks on other susceptible plants. Use slug pellets every few weeks, especially in spring and autumn.

There is now a vogue for seed-raised plants, some of them F1 hybrids, which makes them relatively expensive. After two or more years in the garden I cannot see very much difference between the F1 and the older 'unimproved' types. Another improvement, depending on your point of view, is the availability of pink and red seed-raised plants. These are now commonly available in garden centres.

A. deltoidea 'Dr Mules' Deep violet-blue, probably the most commonly grown variety.
'Variegata' Less vigorous and a tidier grower than the green-leaved types. The marginal variegation makes a very pretty contrast with the violet-blue flowers. A fine garden plant.

* **Berberis** (Barberry) Nec/Pol Shr. 🐝
full sun, semi-shade

The popularity and variability of these splendid shrubs, which range in height from one foot to well over ten feet (30 cm - 3 m), cannot be denied. Garden centres carry a wide range, and specialist nurseries may stock 150 or more. All the species are very attractive to honey bees, and large shrubs will be abuzz with bees when in flower, some collecting the greenish-yellow pollen, others the abundant, good quality nectar.

The drooping clusters of individual flowers appear in spring along the entire length of either stiffly erect or gently arching branches. The evergreen types generally have showier flowers than the deciduous ones, and these may be yellow, orange or orange-red, rarely exceeding ⅓ in (8 mm) in diameter, and cup-and-saucer shaped. There are six sepals, and all the flower parts are of the same colour. The stamens are sensitive to touch, and when bees probe for the nectar, held in six separate nectaries at the base of the petals, pollen is 'dabbed' on the bee's proboscis, thus ensuring cross-pollination when another flower is visited.

Berberis usually flower so freely that the very condensed side shoots (which appear as single leaves or rosettes) from which the flowers arise, may be obscured. Likewise, the not infrequently vicious spines, which may be up to 3 in (7.5 cm) long — the epithet 'prickle' or 'thorn' simply does not do them full justice! The spines are usually in threes (although there may be two other rudimentary ones), and form a T shape, joining the stem at the head of the T.

The clusters of berries start to appear in early autumn, and in some species and cultivars disappear very quickly, due to the depredations of blackbirds in particular, before any real coloration is noticeable. *Berberis darwinii* is particularly susceptible to these attacks, even

though one might think its small dark purple-black berries would not appear as attractive to birds as the beautiful eye-catching, coral-red, translucent berries of *Berberis wilsoniae*. Yet this is one of the last to be stripped by birds. Beauty is, in this case, obviously more than skin deep! The fruits rarely exceed ¼ in (6 mm) in diameter, and may be spherical or oval. Leaf shapes vary from the long narrow ones of *B. x stenophylla* to the elliptic shape of *B. candidula*. The autumn colours of the deciduous species and cultivars can be stunning, with brilliant reds and oranges predominating, whilst many of the evergreens are a perfect foil for the bright flowers of a range of other plants.

A fair number of the *Berberis* are vigorous growers and will quickly smother other less strongly growing neighbours, so unless you have plenty of space, limit your choice to the less vigorous types. Most of the deciduous types are tolerant of windy exposed situations, and are useful for hedging or as a first line of defence for more delicate subjects.

B. buxifolia 'Nana' ht: 2 ft *60 cm* dist: 18

Berberis x lologensis, a natural hybrid between B. darwinii and B. linearifolia. .

in *45 cm* Apr-May. A slow-growing, mound-forming plant with purple berries in autumn.

B. x carminea 'Buccaneer' ht: 5 ft *1.5 m* dist: 4 ft *1.25 m* Jun-Jul. The smallish leaves colour well in autumn, and are complemented by the large deep red berries which are carried well into the winter.

B. candidula ht: 2 ft *60 cm* dist: 18 in *45 cm* May-Jun. Densely mounded growth habit, with dark green leaves, silver grey beneath. Flowers are bright yellow followed by purplish fruits in autumn.

B. darwinii ht: 7 ft *2.25 m* dist: 5 ft *1.5 m* Apr-May. With its small glossy, holly-like leaves and scented orange-yellow flowers, this is a deservedly popular species. The purple berries are usually taken early by birds.

B. gagnepainii ht: 6 ft *2 m* dist: 4 ft *1.25 m* May-Jun. The dark green leaves, which are normally lance-shaped, may be up to 4 in (10

49

cm) long. The pale yellow flowers are invariably followed by masses of blackish berries with a purple bloom.

B. julianae 🐝 ☁ ht: 9 ft *2.75 m* dist: 6-7 ft *2-2.25 m* May. A strong dense grower, the stems heavily spined. The young spiny leaves are coppery at first, whilst some of the older leaves frequently turn reddish in autumn. The pale yellow scented flowers are followed by oval black fruits, with a blue bloom.

B. linearifolia 'Orange King' 🐝 ⚘ ht: 7 ft *2.25 m* dist: 4-5 ft *1.25-1.5 m* Apr-May. The stiffly erect form of this cultivar would discourage many from wanting it in their own garden — that is, until they have seen the flowers. These are a rich orange and have the deepest coloration of any of the *Berberis*. There may occasionally be the bonus of a second, but less vigorous, flowering season in the autumn. The berries are black with a purple bloom, whilst the leaves are dark green above and grey beneath.

References to this plant not being completely hardy puzzle me, for the specimen of which I write stands within 25 yards of an official meteorological station that recorded temperatures of below 14°F (-10°C) in February 1984 on several occasions, without damage to the plant.

B. x stenophylla 🐝 ☁ ht: 9 ft *2.75 m* dist: 7-9 ft *2.25-2.75 m* Apr-May. A big garden will be required to give this marvellous plant full rein. Grown as a specimen it will grow wider than it is high, its arching branches literally wreathed with the scented bright orange-yellow flowers, the dark green linear leaves seemingly nowhere in evidence. The black berries are not such an impressive spectacle. For those with less space, try one of the dwarfer forms of *x stenophylla* listed below.

'Crawley Gem' 🐝 ☁ ht: 3 ft *1 m* dist: 2 ft *60 cm* May. Flowers orange-red, berries black.

'Corallina Compacta' 🐝 ☁ ht: 18 in *45 cm* dist: 12-18 in *30-45 cm* May-Jun. A neat little plant with tight clusters of small matt green leaves contrasting well with its coral red flower buds, which open to a deep yellow.

'Semperflorens' 🐝 ☁ ht: 3 ft *1 m* dist: 2 ft *60 cm* May-Jun. This cultivar has a longer flowering season than the type, and this should endear it to beekeepers, if they can find it on offer!

The bulk of the deciduous *Berberis* come from the single genus *thunbergii*, which has some very diverse and worthy cultivars to its name, all of which flower in April-May, and have small rounded leaves which colour well in autumn.

Berberis thunbergii 'Atropurpurea' is a graceful plant with very attractive purplish foliage, changing to red in autumn.

B. thunbergii 'Atropurpurea' ⚘ ☁ ht: 5 ft *1.5 m* dist: 4 ft *1.25 m*. This handsome and graceful shrub is seen less frequently now that the more strongly coloured (and to my mind more vulgar) and stiffly erect cultivars such as 'Red Chief' and 'Red Pillar' are the darlings of the garden centres. In my own garden the purplish leaves contrast well with the yellow stonecrop which has taken over the ground beneath, where little else will grow. The flowers are a pale orange and are followed by glistening bright red oval berries, rather profusely borne.

For those with less space the dwarf form 'Atropurpurea Nana' is a very acceptable substitute.

'Aurea' ⅄ ◌ ht: 3 ft *1 m* dist: 2 ft *60 cm*. The lovely lemon yellow-green foliage of this cultivar makes it one of my favourite plants, but it does need sun for the foliage to colour well, and shelter if it is not to be scorched. Bright red berries in autumn.

'Harlequin' ⅄ ◌ ht: 5 ft *1.5 m* dist: 4 ft *1.25 m*. A not unattractive and very popular pink-leaved form with white splashes; more showy than the older cultivar 'Rose Glow'. Red berries in autumn.

B. wilsoniae ⅄ ◌ ht: 4 ft *1.25 m* dist: 4 ft *1.25 m*. No-one would grow this species for its form, leaf colour or pale yellow flowers alone; but the brilliant translucent coral-red berries produced in tight clusters all along the branches that hang on well into the winter give it, for me, an edge over any of the other *Berberis*. Nothing could look more deliciously edible than the fruits of this species. The sea green leaves also give good autumn colour.

Bergenia Pol. ⚘ H. ◌
Mar-May, full sun, semi-shade
Easily grown, large shiny-leaved evergreens, with good autumn leaf coloration and showy ½-¾ in (12-20 mm) diameter flowers of pink, or red, but also white and pale primrose.

Bergenias, with their clumps of broadly ovate leaves up to 1 ft (30 cm) long, produced from a compact semi-woody rootstock, have few equals as good, all-round garden plants. Marvellously versatile in their own right, they also blend so well with other plant forms that they are indispensable in this respect alone.

The thick-stemmed, frequently wine-coloured flower stems carry bell-shaped flowers, the centres of which are packed with a ring of yellow-tipped stamens, the pollen from which is avidly collected.

B. cordifolia ht: 18 in *45 cm* dist: 18 in *45 cm* Several different coloured forms of this species are seen in cultivation, the most common of which has flowers of a lovely silvery-pink, which last well on into summer.

B. purpurascens 'Ballawley' ht: 2 ft *60 cm* dist: 2 ft *60 cm* Very large leaves which turn a beautiful dull pinky-red in autumn.

'Evening Glow' ht: 18 in *45 cm* dist: 18 in *45 cm* Neat wavy-edged, rounded leaves which colour maroon to plum-red in winter. Flowers semi-double and rose-red, mainly in spring but intermittently through the summer as well. This cultivar would probably be most people's first choice because of the boldness of its leaves and excellent winter leaf coloration.

* Borago officinalis (Borage) Nec/Pol A(h).
⚘
ht: 12-18 in *30-45 cm* dist: 1½-2 ft *45-60 cm* Apr-Oct, full sun, semi-shade
Covered as it is in short stiff hairs, this plant is as unpleasant to handle as an unshaven chin! But the vivid gentian-blue flowers carried in nodding clusters more than compensate for this — they are fabulous. The dark green calyx points project between the pointed petal lobes, creating the effect of a ten-pointed star. The base of each petal is a pale blue and projects upwards slightly, forming, with the ring of five dark-purplish anthers, a 'reservoir' in which nectar accumulates. The leaves may be up to 8 in (20 cm) long.

Borage self-seeds quite happily, even in relatively poor soils, and not infrequently produces a few variegated forms which are even more handsome than the type.

Borage has recently been grown as an agricultural crop on a field scale. Beekeepers who have had bees on these fields are very variable in their assessment of its value as a honey producer, but at times it does produce a good nectar flow.

Buddleia Nec. Shr. ⅄
dry, full sun
Easily grown shrubs thriving under the driest soil conditions, but most species and cultivars are rather large for the small garden. The flower tubes are up to ½ in (8-10 mm) long, and you might think it impossible for the bees to reach the nectar, but extract it they do, the nectar building up in the narrow corolla tubes to allow this.

Buddleia alternifolia,
beautiful in colour,
shape and scent.

B. alternifolia ht: 12 ft *3.5 m* dist: 8-10 ft *2.5-3 m* Jun-Jul. The slender arching branches bear clusters of sweetly scented lilac flowers along their entire length in early summer. The leaves are grey-green and lance-shaped, up to 4 in (10 cm) long. A most elegant and graceful shrub.

B. davidii (Butterfly Bush) ht: 8-12 ft *2.5-3.5 m* dist: 8-10 ft *2.5-3 m* Jul-Sep. A large gaunt shrub with gently arching flower spikes up to 2 ft (60 cm) long. The individual flowers are legion and have a conspicuous orange eye, the very pleasant fragrance attracting butterflies and bees in profusion. The leaves are long and narrow, with fine forward-pointing teeth, dark green above and conspicuously grey beneath.

If left unpruned, the bushes quickly become untidy and the flowers progressively smaller. To prevent this, prune hard back annually in March to within a few buds of the previous season's growth.

'Black Knight' Deep violet flowers.

'Fascination' Bright pink flowers.

'Harlequin' The red-purple flowers contrast nicely with the attractively variegated leaves. A fine plant, with the added bonus that it is less vigorous than its green brethren.

'Royal Red' Very striking deep red-purple flowers.

'White Cloud' White flowers.

B. globosa (Orange Ball Tree) ht: 8-12 ft *2.5-3.5 m* dist: 8-10 ft *2.5-3 m* May-Jun. When it flowers well, *globosa* is a striking plant, but its irregular performances in this respect, coupled with its large size, have kept it from being grown in most private gardens.

The terminal clusters of 1 in (2.5 cm) orange balls are composed of many small flowers with much shorter corolla tubes than other species, affording bees ease of access to the nectar. The long leaves have a 'crinkly' surface and are greyish-green above, grey beneath. Evergreen in mild districts, deciduous in cold ones.

* Calluna vulgaris (Ling or Heather) Nec/Pol Shr.

ht: 18 in *45 cm* dist: 12 in *30 cm*
Jul-Nov, acid, full sun
This straggly dwarf evergreen plant covers very

many thousands of acres of moorland areas throughout Britain and Europe. Rounded or rocky hills covered with purplish pink flowers in August and September are a sight that once seen, is never forgotten. Walking across the springy stems is tiring, but these same stems make a very comfortable seat, and from this close range some variability of flower colour, from white through pink to purple, can clearly be observed. Hopefully, when grown in the private garden, there will be sufficient shelter for the bees to work the flowers in late summer — this is not always the case on windy moorland areas. The small flowers are actually shorter than the calyx, which at under ¼ in (6 mm) long — and wide — is more ornamental and consists of four narrowly oval sepals. The one-sided flower spike may be up to 12 in (30 cm) long. The dead flowers will persist through the winter and are not unattractive.

Individual cultivars flower over about a two-month period between July and November. Most *Calluna* are now pot-grown, so if you are unsure if a plant has single or double flowers, check it out at the nursery or garden centre when in flower, and then make your purchase. Those cultivars with coloured foliage usually flower freely, but before getting carried away, as inevitably you will be if you are warmed by their rich colours on winter days, remember that an acid soil is a must. To help prevent the plants taking on their characteristic straggly appearance, clip the dead flower spikes in spring just before new growth commences.

The much branched stems are densely covered with small overlapping leaves in four rows, giving a distinct quadrangular outline.

Ling honey has been variously described as 'glorious', 'unusual' and 'strong flavoured'. It is also almost unique, there being only three other plants in the world which produce a similar honey. Heather honey, as it is more commonly called, is a jelly, does not crystallize and is somewhat bitter in flavour, rather than sweet. The bouquet is distinctive and can sometimes be detected in a sample of honey which has no visible evidence of containing heather honey. Honey from the *Erica* heathers is different, and does not gel, and it is usually called bell heather honey.

'Alba Aurea' Aug-Sep. A white-flowered form which has yellow-tipped foliage.

A cultivar of Calluna vulgaris. Callunas are extremely popular garden plants, but they must have an acid soil.

'Alportii Praecox' Flowers crimson, borne early July/August.

'Blazeaway' Aug-Sep. Flowers lilac-mauve, the green foliage changing to a rich red bronze in winter. Stunning.

'Hibernica' Oct-Nov. Flowers of mauve, very freely borne and often obscuring the foliage of this very compact form.

'Pallida' Aug-Sep. Flowers of pale pink.

'Serlei Aurea' Oct-Nov. Flowers white in long racemes, with golden foliage.

Caltha palustris (Marsh Marigold/King-cups) Nec/Pol H. ≢

ht: 12 in *30 cm* dist: 18 in *45 cm*
Mar-Jun, wet, full sun, semi-shade
Before the days of the agricultural 'rip out hedges and drain every spare corner of land' brigade in Britain, and similar movements in some parts of Europe, the marsh marigold reigned supreme in just about every marshy corner, along with the cuckoo pint, marsh orchid and primrose. They were all part of the country scene, and it is sad that they are all now so diminished in number. However, there are still good populations in marshy places, and even at the edge of fast-flowing streams, where there may be quite marked changes in water level.

The flowers have 5-8 rounded petals and are borne in lax leafy clusters on semi-erect hollow stems arising from a stout creeping rhizome. As with most buttercup-like plants, the flowers glisten in strong light, and groups of marsh marigolds provide a brilliant splash of gold in wet spring meadows. The rounded leaves are also shiny, and up to 4 in (10 cm) in length. Honey and bumble bees work the golden flowers with great relish, taking away nectar and large loads of bright yellow pollen. They often use the lowest leaves as landing sites when collecting water. *Caltha* must have a very moist or boggy soil, and will even thrive under water to a maximum depth of 9 in (23 cm).

'Alba' is a white form with a yellow centre, insipid in comparison with the species, but appealing to some.

* Campanula (Bell Flower) Nec/Pol
full sun, semi-shade
Surely one of the most versatile, easily grown and free-flowering of all herbaceous and alpine plants. Although predominantly blue, you can find white, pink and pale-yellow flowered species. All are attractive to bees, the larger forms providing a bountiful source of pollen.

The generic name (which the common name also reflects) is in fact a description of the flower shape. These may be shallowly bell-shaped or more tubular, with only minimal reflexing of the five petals. The alpine types in particular bear their erect or nodding flowers on such delicate stems that the slightest breeze will set them prettily in motion.

In the text I have divided them up into alpine and herbaceous (including biennial) types.

ALPINE TYPES H. ≢

The more vigorous types such as *C. muralis* can, of course, be used at the front of herbaceous or mixed borders if required, but they do look best in dry walls, screes and rock gardens.

C. barbata (Bearded Bell Flower) ht: 6 in *15 cm* dist: 6 in *15 cm* Jun. Not commonly seen in cultivation, regrettably, for the nodding 1 in (2.5 cm) pale blue flower bells have showy, conspicuous, pale blue hairs within, but not so thick as to prevent bee access.

The hairy leaves which arise from a basal rosette are oblong lance-shaped with wavy margins.

C. carpatica ht: 9 in *23 cm* dist: 1 ft *30 cm* Jun-Sep. The upturned 'open' flowers, 1¼ in (3 cm) in diameter, are carried singly, and are blue or white, depending on cultivar. The basal leaves are oval and toothed, similar to those of the other species listed, whilst the stem leaves are grass-like.

C. cochlearifolia ht: 4 in *10 cm* dist: 1 ft *30 cm* Jun-Sep. Smaller, daintier, more bell-shaped blue flowers (two to six per stem) than *carpatica*. The cultivar 'Alba' has white flowers.

C. muralis syn. *portenschlagiana* ht: 6 in *15 cm* dist: 1 ft *30 cm* Jun-Sep. The ¾ in (2 cm) pale blue flowers, which are carried in great profusion, are quite open, with rather pointed petals.

There are a host of other cultivars suitable for rock gardens, as any alpine catalogue will reveal. Fortunately it would be difficult to make a bad choice, both as far as your bees or your garden are concerned.

HERBACEOUS AND BIENNIAL TYPES

Many of these more robust species and cultivars are suitable not only for herbaceous borders but for mixed borders, where they will compete quite strongly for space. The leaves are generally toothed and lance-shaped with rounded bases.

C. x burghaltii H. ht: 18 in *45 cm* dist: 1 ft *30 cm* Jun and Sep. The deep-purple, 3 in (7.5 cm) long flower buds open to pale blue.

C. glomerata (Clustered Bell Flower) H. ht: 18 in *45 cm* dist: 2 ft *60 cm* Jun-Sep. A rather stiffly erect plant with rough leaves, carrying its violet-purple, 1-2 in (2.5-5.cm) star-like flowers in tight terminal clusters. Bold and handsome, if rather less graceful than other species. A white-flowered form is available.

C. lactiflora H. ht: 5 ft *1.5 m* dist: 3 ft *1 m* Jul-Sep. Rather open flowers 1 in (2.5 cm) or so wide, in crowded heads of palest blue.

'Alba' White flowers.

'Prichard's Variety' Deep violet-blue flowers.

C. latifolia H. ht: 4 ft *1.25 m* dist: 2 ft *60 cm* Jun-Jul. Multi-directional, 2 in (5 cm) bell-shaped flowers, powder blue, carried in elegantly tapered spikes. The white form 'Alba' is slightly less vigorous.

'Gloaming' Very pale blue.

C. medium (Canterbury Bell) Bien. ht: 18 in *45 cm* dist: 1 ft *30 cm* May-Jul. Bells 2 in (5 cm) long, of blue, pink or white. The aptly named Cup and Saucer types are now the most commonly seen, although these 'odd coloured daffodils' do not appeal to my tastes. It is, however, rather nice to see Canterbury Bells come back into gardens once again, for there is an indefinable cottage garden feel to them, and they look perfect set amongst a jumble of other plants.

C. poscharskyana H. ht: 1 ft *30 cm* dist: 2 ft *60 cm* May-Sep. Lavender-blue 1 in (2.5 cm) star-shaped flowers. It spreads quickly — a superb plant.

Castanea sativa (Sweet or Spanish Chestnut) Nec/Pol T.
ht: 90-100 ft *27-30 m*
Jul, acid, full sun
Far too large in its maturity for any but the biggest garden, but a common enough tree on neutral or acid soils in warmer parts of Europe and Britain. It is sometimes 'cropped' as a coppice tree, for which its growth habit and wood quality is ideally suited. It is not normally regarded as a fast grower, but when coppiced there are few other trees that can keep pace with it. The sweet chestnut is the longest-lived of all deciduous trees, and develops a deeply fissured bark that spirals around the trunk.

The handsome glossy saw-toothed leaves are conspicuously veined and may be up to 10 in (25 cm) long and 3½ in (8.5 cm) wide. They are very persistent even after they fall in autumn; so persistent in fact that in parts of Europe they are used as 'baking plates' and 'wraps' for brioches.

The male and female flowers are borne on separate catkins in the leaf axils of the young shoots, the males being up to 9 in (23 cm) in length. Although the individual, pale yellow-green catkins are inconspicuous, their sheer volume turns the tree into a distinct and showy sight.

Heavy crops of the brown shiny chestnuts are rarely produced in Britain, unless there is a hot dry summer (an all too infrequent occurrence). Bees work the trees very heavily for pollen, which is very small in size and consequently often found in some quantity in honey. In warm weather there is a good nectar flow, and this is produced in quantity in warmer areas such as Spain. The prickly green cases that enclose the chestnuts need no description — for who has not suffered a few pricks trying to extract the nuts. Pigs, however, seem to have little or no such trouble, and in parts of Corsica, where wild pigs still abound, the flavour of their meat testifies to this.

The cultivar 'Marron De Lyon' is regarded as the best fruiting cultivar.

Ceanothus thrysiflorus repens. Somewhat tender, but a splendid shrub if it likes your garden. Visited chiefly for pollen by the bees.

Ceanothus Nec/Pol Shr. 🌣
full sun

The Californian lilacs are not the hardiest of shrubs, but once you have seen them in frothy full flower you will find it difficult to resist trying to grow them, albeit against a wall for protection. Take a few cuttings each summer as an insurance policy against a hard winter's frosts.

The flower spikes are packed with tiny, usually blue, flowers. From between the incurving sepals emerge the five ladle-like petals, each with one yellow-tipped stamen. The stigma emerges from the centre of the calyx. The individual flower stalks take on the colour of the flower, adding considerably to the overall effect, as do the glossy leaves, particularly of the evergreen types.

Most are lime tolerant, but will not do well on shallow chalky soils. The evergreen species are less tolerant of salt spray than their deciduous counterparts. Only species or cultivars that are regarded as reasonably hardy are listed below, but you may feel inclined to try others.

EVERGREENS

'Autumnal Blue' 🐝 ht: 6 ft *2 m* dist: 4-5 ft *1.25-*

1.5 m May-Sep. Possibly the hardiest of the evergreen cultivars. Flowers medium blue in spikes, about 3½ in (9 cm) long.

'Southmead' ht: 6 ft *2 m* dist: 4-5 ft *1.25-1.5 m* May. Has a dense habit of growth, with bright blue flowers.

C. thrysiflorus ht: 8-10 ft *2.5-3 m* dist: 6-7 ft *2-2.25 m* May-Jun. Rich blue flowers borne in early summer. A large plant that will eventually reach 20 ft (6 m) or more. The mound-forming *repens* — a form of *thrysiflorus* — grows to only about 18 in (45 cm), making it more suitable for the smaller garden.

DECIDUOUS

'Gloire de Versailles' ht: 6 ft *2 m* dist: 4-5 ft *1.25-1.5 m* Jul-Sep, salt tol. By far the most widely grown cultivar, and deservedly so. Very large flower spikes of light blue.

'Marie Simon' ht: 6 ft *2 m* dist: 4-5 ft *1.25-1.5 m* Jul-Sep, salt tol. Pink flowers.

'Perle Rose' ht: 6 ft *2 m* dist: 4-5 ft *1.25-1.5 m* Jul-Sep, salt tol. A paler pink than 'Marie Simon'.

'Topaz' ht: 6 ft *2 m* dist: 4-5 ft *1.25-1.5 m* Jul-Sep, salt tol. Bright blue flowers.

Centaurea Nec/Pol

full sun

Handsome plants, not unlike de-prickled thistles. The rounded or oval 'heads' (from the top of which erupt the flowers) are made up of overlapping bracts which are prettily fringed, rather like eyelashes. In some species the dark spots on the bracts exude nectar, and honey bees can clearly be seen gently probing for this — even preferring unopened buds to those in full flower.

The individual florets of the flowers are tubular, with five shallow lobes, the outer ones usually much longer than the inner ones, sometimes making access to the nectar impossible for the bee.

There is a large number of native species (in Britain and Europe usually known as knapweeds or hardheads) that really are best left in the wild. Being late flowering, these plants have suffered particularly badly from verge mowing in the past, but are now making a comeback, especially on calcareous soils, where they thrive. The honey of knapweed is extremely strong in flavour, reminding me of cough mixture, and is useful when blending honey. Useful loads of white pollen are readily collected.

C. candidissima syn. *rutifolia* and *cineraria* First-class grey foliage plants usually grown as annuals, although they are in fact perennial. They are rather tender and only worth growing long-term in milder coastal districts, where they will produce flowers after their second growing season from seed. Do not attempt to divide up plants.

C. cyanus (Cornflower) A(h). 🌿 A charming plant with grey strap-shaped leaves and 1¼ in (3 cm) dark blue flowers. Many of the newer cultivars bred from *cyanus* are excellent in colour, range and form, but unfortunately have 'double' flowers which, from the bees' point of view, means a larger proportion of longer tubular ray-florets with inaccessible nectar sources.

'Polka Dot Mixed' ht: 18 in *45 cm* dist: 9 in *23 cm* Jun-Oct. A superb mixture of white, pink, blue, red and mauve flowers up to 2 in (5 cm) in diameter.

C. hypocleuca 'John Coutts' H. ⬭ ht: 2 ft *60 cm* dist: 18 in *45 cm* Jun-Jul. Large 3 in (7.5 cm) pink flowers with a yellow eye and much divided grey-green leaves.

'Steenbergii' H. ⬭ ht: 2 ft *60 cm* dist: 18 in *45 cm* Jul-Sep. Crimson flowers with a white eye.

C. macrocephala H. ⬭ ht: 4 ft *1.25 m* dist: 3 ft *1 m* Aug-Oct. A quite distinct species with 3½ in (9 cm) bright yellow flower heads, and shiny, dark brown, papery bud-scales. Well worth growing.

C. montana H. ⬭ ht: 2 ft *60 cm* dist: 18 in *45 cm* Jun-Oct. The distinct dark brown extra-floral nectaries are quite apparent on this species. The blue ray florets form a single rather sparse ring which accentuates the dull red centre, giving a most effective colour contrast. The winged stems, which bear lance-shaped to oval leaves, add the final touch to one of the best of all herbaceous plants. There are white, pink and red forms to choose from.

Centaurea cyanus, a delightful survivor from the cornfields of the pre-hormone-weedkiller period.

C. moschata (Sweet Sultan) A(h). ht: 18 in *45 cm* dist: 9 in *23 cm* Jun-Sep. The 2 in (5 cm) fragrant flower heads of this species are rather more spikey than others, giving a powder-puff-like effect in yellow, pink, white, carmine and rose —irresistible!

Cercis siliquastrum Nec/Pol T.

ht: 10-12 ft *3-3.5 m* dist: 12-15 ft *3.5-4.5 m*
May-Jun, full sun

Most commonly known as the Judas Tree, this densely twiggy plant will form a small tree if encouraged, but left to its own devices it is much happier as a large rounded shrub. Given a warmer climate, however, it can easily reach 50 ft (15 m) or so. The small vivid, pinky-purple, pea-like flowers are borne in profusion on young and old branches alike, and also directly on the main trunks and branches, often before any leaves have been produced. For brightness of flower colour *Cercis* has few equals; there are unfortunately many poor seed-raised plants with weak flowering habits in cultivation.

The flowers, which are very attractive to bees, are followed by clusters of red-brown pods up to 4 in (10 cm) in length. There is a white form, 'Alba', and a much darker one, 'Bodnant', with deep purple flowers.

Although it will thrive on heavier soils, drainage must be good.

Chaenomeles Nec/Pol Shr.

ht: 4-5 ft *1.25-1.5 m* dist: 4-5 ft *1.25-1.5 m*
Mar-Jun, full sun, shade

You may in the past (and will certainly again in the future) have heard *Chaenomeles* referred to as quince, *Cydonia* or *Japonica*. Call it what you will, it is a deservedly popular shrub, with its long flowering season and attractive fruits borne on densely twiggy and thorny shoots.

The flowers, up to 1½ in (4 cm) in diameter, are borne in tight clusters in the early spring and summer, and the bright red and orange cultivars in particular make a warm sight on cold March days. Being a somewhat untidy grower, *Chaenomeles* is most often seen planted against a wall, where it is 'contained' by regular spur pruning. This includes cutting back all

those side shoots produced the previous summer to 2 in (5 cm) or so in February. This not only keeps the plants within bounds but also allows a clear view of the flowers. These are five-petalled and spoon-shaped, with numerous anthers making a conspicuous and attractive feature. Odd flowers can be found at just about any time of year. Grown as wall shrubs, an area of 9 x 9 ft (7.5 sq m) will be covered without too much difficulty in four to five years.

After flowering, the aromatic, hard yellow quinces are produced. These may be 2 in (5 cm) in diameter, but can be as large as 7 in (18 cm) in vigorous species such as *cathayensis*. In a mild winter the fruits will persist right through to the spring.

The finely toothed, rounded leaves vary in shape and have attractive reddish hues when young. Not a shrub I would want to be without.

C. speciosa 'Moerloosii' The flowers are a delicate pink and white.

'Nivalis' Pure white flowers.

C. x superba 'Crimson and Gold' Crimson petals with prominent golden anthers.

'Ball of Fire' Orangey-red flowers.

'Knap Hill Scarlet' Bright orange-scarlet flowers freely produced.

* Cheiranthus (Wallflower) Nec/Pol Bien. H.

salt tol, full sun

For as long as anyone can remember, wall-flowers were the gardeners' favourite for bedding out in autumn, when the summer bedding plants were over. This has now changed, and most of what would have been beds of wallflowers are planted instead with plants that give autumn, winter and spring colour, such as winter-flowering pansies, poly-anthus and daisies. This is not too difficult to understand, since the wallflower is a rather boring plant from October to April, but in April and May the display is marvellous and I cannot keep my nose out of the deliciously fragrant flowers — a fragrance which will pervade the whole garden on warm still days.

No wonder bees are attracted in large numbers. The four-petalled flowers are carried in terminal spikes which will go on flowering until June if allowed to do so, but they are usually ripped out by the impatient gardener and replaced with geraniums, alyssum and lobelia. Wallflowers are then usually treated as biennials, but they are in fact perennial and several vegetatively propagated named cultivars are available.

C. x alionii syn. *Erysimum x alionii* ht: 12 in *30 cm* dist: 9-12 in *23-30 cm* Apr-May. Botanically this plant is more correctly known as *Erysimum* (it has six nectaries instead of two as in *Cheiranthus*), but to most of us it is still known as the Siberian wallflower. The flowers are bright vibrant orange, and are borne in slightly rounded heads. Apricot and lemon yellow cultivars are also available.

C. cheiri ht: 6-18 in *15-45 cm* dist: 6-12 in *15-30 cm* Apr-May. The colour range is wide, as any flower seed catalogue of cultivars will tell you: 'Blood Red', 'Cloth of Gold', 'Primrose Monarch', 'Ruby Gem', 'Scarlet Bedder' and 'Ivory White', to name but a few. Most gardeners now prefer the more dwarf bedding cultivars at around 12-15 in (30-40 cm), or even the so-called Tom Thumb types at 6-9 in (15-23 cm).

Two long-flowering, vegetatively propagated cultivars suitable for the herbaceous border, rock garden or dry wall crevice are:

'Bowles Mauve' ht: 2 ft *60 cm* dist: 12-18 in *30-45 cm* Apr-Aug. The rich purple flowers are shown to advantage against the dark green foliage.

'Moonlight' ht: 6 in *15 cm* dist: 6 in *15 cm* Apr-Aug. Lemon yellow flowers.

Chionodoxa Nec/Pol B/C.

ht: 6 in *15 cm* dist: 3 in *7.5 cm*
Feb-Apr, full sun, semi-shade
The English translation of this difficult name is 'Glory of the Snow', and how well named it is, standing up to severe frost, snow and gales without damage or the need to close up its pale blue and white flowers for protection, as many other plants do. They grow well in short grass

and look particularly good at the edges of borders of spring-flowering shrubs such as *Forsythia*. They thrive and quickly colonize under a very wide range of conditions, compacted gravel drives and paths, or the bases of walls in sun or shade, being favoured locations.

Most of the species are less than 6 in (15 cm) in height, but can rise above this if they are grown through low ground cover such as *Erica herbacea*. What a contrast these two plants make, particularly when one of the dark red, winter/spring flowering cultivars is chosen, and how spoilt for choice are the bees that find these two plants growing together!

After flowering, copious quantities of seed are normally set, and these green to red 'marbles' (seed pods) cause the flower stem to collapse under their weight. The pods are not unattractive, and eventually will be responsible for new colonies of seedlings which will be produced close to the parent plant. Where more than one species is grown, hybridization appears to occur freely, resulting in variable offspring. This may be one of the reasons why the nomenclature of this species, particularly in the bulb trade, is so confused.

The bulbs should be planted 3 in (7 cm) deep, as soon as they become available in autumn.

C. luciliae Most of the bulbs sold bear this name, probably incorrectly. If you purchase them you will almost certainly get a robust 8-10 in (20-25 cm) flower spike bearing 6-10 blue flowers with largish white centres. Each flower will measure approximately 1 in (2.5 cm) across.

C. sardensis Smaller, earlier flowering and more dainty than *luciliae*, being only 5 in (12.5 cm) or so high, with up to twelve ½ in (1 cm) flowers with a small white eye.

Choisya ternata (Mexican Orange Blossom)

Pol. Shr. 🐝 ☁
ht: 5 ft *1.5 m* dist: 6 ft *2 m*
May-Jun and Aug-Sep, full sun, semi-shade
A most handsome shrub with deep green trifoliate leaves, each shiny leaflet up to 3 in (7.5 cm) in length and emitting a pungent odour when bruised.

Bee plants — Cirsium

The pure white flowers, 1½ in (3.5 cm) in diameter, have seven petals and these do not overlap, giving a propellor-like impression. The stalks of the stamens, which vary in number and length, are also pure white, tipped with yellow anthers which curve inwards slightly over the sceptre-like ovary. Beauty enough, but the wonderful fragrance, like orange blossom, is the crown to add to the sceptre.

Give it a sheltered spot, preferably close to a path or the house so the fragrance can be readily enjoyed. *Choisya* is hardy in most parts of Britain and western Europe, but it can be severely damaged or even killed during prolonged periods of severe frost; fortunately cuttings taken in August root easily.

Cistus x corbariensis. All the rock roses are great pollen plants, thriving in sunny and dryish conditions.

Cirsium Nec/Pol H.
ht: 3 ft *1 m* dist: 2 ft *60 cm*
Jun-Sep

Far and few are those that welcome thistles into their gardens, but they are attractive and interesting flowers, and in many cases, where the narrow flower tubes are short enough, produce a good supply of late-season nectar for the honey bee. All you have to remember when growing them is to remove the old flower heads before the seeds mature and float like 'thistle down' to every corner of your, and everyone else's, garden.

Less invasive are the cultivated types, of which only two species are usually seen, both of which have typical thistle-like leaves.

C. japonicum Flowers pink to purple, up to 2 in (5 cm) in diameter.

C. rivulare 'Atropurpureum' Flowers dull red-purple up to 1½ in (3.5 cm) in diameter singly, or in terminal clusters on 'woolly' stems.

Although the Scottish thistle is actually an *Onopordum*, I include it here as a really worthwhile plant of statuesque form. Up to 6 ft (1.8 m) high, with its winged spiny grey leaves and flower stems, there is no grander plant. For sheer impact I rate it alongside the Himalayan poppy, and like this latter plant it is very attractive to bees.

Cistus (Rock or Sun Rose) Nec/Pol Shr.
Jun-Jul, dry, salt tol, full sun

To see just one *Cistus* in full flower on a sunny day, loaded with pollen-covered bees, is enough to captivate most people and start them off collecting a range of these beautiful free-flowering plants; but to see hillsides and sea cliffs covered with them, as is common in Spain and Portugal, southern France and the Mediterranean islands, is breathtaking.

The large central boss of stamens is invariably yellow and always contrasts well with the petals, be they white, rose-pink, purple or shades in between. Many species also have a distinctive ¼-½ in (6-13 mm) blotch, usually dull red, at the base of each of the five petals. The satiny petals of the larger-flowered species are somewhat crinkled, like poppies, which presumably helps to strengthen and support them. The flowers will not open at all unless they receive direct sunlight, so choose a spot for your plants carefully; they also thrive best on dryish soils. The buds of many species colour well prior to opening, and are attractive in their own right; in some species they, and the leaves, are also sticky.

Severe winters will kill off even large mature specimens, but they are easily propagated by cuttings taken in August.

C. x corbariensis ht: 3 ft *1 m* dist: 3-4 ft *1-1.25 m* This is my own particular favourite. The dark sage-green leaves are up to 1½ in (3.5 cm) long, and the pure white flowers are small in comparison with other species, but compensate for this by sheer volume of numbers. Hardier than most species, but certainly not completely hardy.

C. x cyprius ht: 6 ft *2 m* dist: 4 ft *1.25 m* Clusters of 3½ in (9 cm) pure white flowers with crimson blotches.

C. x purpureus ht: 5 ft *1.5 m* dist: 4 ft *1.25 m* The 4 in (10 cm) rose-crimson flowers have dark brown blotches at the petal bases. A very showy plant.

C. x 'Silver Pink' Perhaps the most widely available hybrid, with 3½ in (9 cm) silver-pink flowers.

Clematis Pol.
full sun

Perhaps the most exotic and interesting of all the climbing plants, with something for everyone's taste, both with regard to flower size and colour. Not all, however, are climbers: some interesting herbaceous types are also cultivated. No nectaries as such are present, although some species exude nectar from the mass of stamen stalks. The stamens in all species are yellow or pale lemon, and are a distinctive feature, contrasting well with the flower colour. The long anthers produce large quantities of pollen, and under suitably warm conditions the flowers may be worked for both nectar and pollen.

The elegant divided leaves are always carried in opposite pairs, and in the climbing species have long stalks that twine vigorously round anything with which they come into contact. In

Clematis montana 'Rubens', well worked by bees for pollen. Ivy, when in its flowering phase, is a very valuable late source of nectar and pollen.

deciduous species only the leaflets drop in the autumn, leaving the stalk to harden as it dries, to act as a long-term support — anyone who has tried to untangle clematis branches when pruning will testify to the efficacy of these seemingly weak 'anchors'.

In spite of their reputation for requiring cool roots (conditions they naturally obtain by growing near the bases of trees), most will thrive as long as not in a 'hot spot' and able to get their feet into moist (but not wet or soggy) soil. Clematis also certainly have a preference for alkaline soils, and few if any Old Man's Beard (*Clematis vitalba*), which is native to most of Europe, will be seen in the wild where the pH is much below 6.5.

C. alpina ht: 6 ft *2 m* May. Lantern-shaped nodding blue flowers 2 in (5 cm) long, the petals of which are pointed. The outer stamens are infertile and strap-shaped. It is an ideal plant for trailing over a dwarf wall, or for clambering through shrubs. Makes a very

Clematis armandii, a somewhat tender evergreen climber which looks magnificent growing on walls or up trees in mild areas.

pretty combination with the soft yellow and gently arching habit of *Cytisus x praecox*. Red, pink and white cultivars are also available. Pruning is not essential, but *alpina* can be a vigorous beast on good soil, so may need shearing back.

C. armandii 'Apple Blossom' ht: 12-15 ft *3.5-4.5 m* Apr-May. An irresistible evergreen with dark leathery leaves, against which the marvellous axillary clusters of white pink-shaded flowers can be viewed. Definitely needs the shelter of a warm wall in northern districts, and even this may not be enough to prevent some frost damage. No pruning required.

C. heracleifolia H. ht: 3-4 ft *1-1.25 m* dist: 3 ft *1 m* Aug-Sep. Fragrant flowers with pale blue, recurved petals. Needs staking.

C. integrifolia H. ht: 2 ft *60 cm* dist: 18 in *45 cm* Jun-Aug. Blue lantern-shaped flowers 1½ in (3.5 cm) across.

C. x jackmanii ht: 15 ft *4.5 m* Jul-Oct. Stunning violet-blue flowers up to 5½ in (14 cm) or so in diameter, produced singly or in threes. In February, cut back flowered shoots either to

just above ground level or to within a couple of buds, or to where they were pruned to the previous season. This hybrid, together with the bulk of large flowered hybrids, does not produce any nectar.

C. montana ht: 30 ft *9 m* May. A vigorous and often rampant species ideal for covering even large trees to a height of 20-30 ft (6-9 m) without difficulty, and so effectively that one is often at a loss to identify the host! Walls, sheds, old cars and other eyesores it will cover with equal ease, regardless of aspect — and what a superb plant this is, flowering so freely year after year without any attention. *C. montana* itself is white and is not that common, most people preferring the pink flowered form, 'Rubens', with its bronzy leaves and shoots. Prune, if you need to, immediately after flowering, cutting flowered shoots back to within a couple of buds of the main framework.

The large flowered hybrids are the gardener's favourite, because of their massive 5-9 in (13-23 cm) diameter flowers and their moderate vigour. Many cultivars are available, of which three are listed below.

'Mrs Cholmondely' ht: 10-15 ft *3-4.5 m* May-Sep. Large pale-blue flowers with pointed petals. Prune back to within a foot or so of ground level in February.

'Nelly Moser' ⅄ ⅜ ht: 10-15 ft *3-4.5 m* May-Jun.Pale pink flowers with a wide carmine bar to each petal. Goes over very quickly if planted in hot, dry situations, but there may be a second flush of flowers in September. The most popular cultivar of all. Trim back flowered shoots after flowering.

'Ville de Lyon' ⅄ ⅜ ht: 10-15 ft *3-4.5 m* Jul-Oct. Bright carmine red flowers. Prune as for 'Mrs Cholmondely'.

C. tangutica ⅄ ⅜ ht: 15 ft *4.5 m* Aug-Oct. Ideal for clambering over trees, shrubs and fences. Has small yellow lantern-shaped flowers rather like *alpina*. The fluffy silvery seed heads, carried right through the autumn and winter, are a joy to behold. No pruning is required.

Colutea Nec/Pol Shr. ⅄ ⅊

Jun-Sep, salt tol, full sun
Without the clusters of shiny silvery-brown seed pods rustling in the winter breeze, I doubt this very ordinary shrub tucked away at the back of a large mixed border would have attracted my attention or interest. Hidden as it was for the most part in summer, the pods stood out clearly against the dark background of yew in winter. A Mediterranean shrub, it has become naturalized in some more northerly areas, and is common on rough ground around London and the Thames estuary in England, where beekeepers are finding it a good forage plant for both nectar and pollen.

The Bladder Sennas, as they are known, are easily grown and have pea-like flowers and much-divided leaves.

C. arborescens ht: 10 ft *3 m* dist: 6 ft *2 m* Individual flowers ¾ in (2 cm) long, bright yellow-orange.

Coreopsis Nec/Pol ⅊

Jun-Sep, full sun
Another of that vast army of easily grown composites, which in their simplest forms — single-coloured with fine grassy foliage — I find irresistible.

C. auriculata 'Superba' H. ht: 2½ ft *75 cm* dist: 2 ft *60 cm* Attractive ragged appearance to the petals, eye dull orange-red.

C. grandiflora 'Goldfink' H. ht: 9 in *23 cm* dist: 9-12 in *23-30 cm* Flowers also ragged, but more evenly so, and clear yellow with a small orange-red eye.

C. verticillata H. ht: 2 ft *60 cm* dist: 18 in *45 cm* The irresistible form referred to in my introduction. Masses of 2 in (5 cm) clear yellow flowers, with pointed petals.

In addition there are several annual cultivars available, the best known of which is perhaps 'Dwarf Dazzler', with its heavily zoned coloration, the eye being so large as to almost swamp the ground colour. Not unlike *Zinnia*.

Cornus (Dogwoods) Nec/Pol

A most variable and decorative genus of plants, some of which, such as the red and yellow stiff-stemmed dogwoods, are well known. Others such as the elegantly tiered *kousa* are all too rarely seen.

The flowers of most species are as unremarkable as they are prolific, but in some the tight clusters of small 4-5 petalled flowers, which provide easy bee access, are surrounded by large showy bracts.

I have divided them into two groups for ease of reference: those with coloured stems, and those with attractive 'flowers' (which are in fact bracts).

COLOURED STEMS ⅄ ⅊ ht: 5 ft *1.5 m* dist: 6-7 ft *2-2.25 m* May-Jun, full sun, semi-shade

There is, of course, much more to this group than the stem coloration. The opposite pairs of leaves, which may be up to 5 in (12.5 cm) long, are handsome in their own right and usually colour up very well in autumn. Those cultivars which also have variegated foliage are particularly showy, providing year-round interest. Unfortunately, if the strong stem coloration is to be retained then the old stems should be cut down to within a few inches of the old wood in March, just before the new growth starts. This of course means no flowers for the bees. Compromise by cutting half the old stems down each year.

63

Although the coloured stems are most often pictured near water, the plants will in fact thrive equally well under dry conditions.

C. alba 'Elegantissima' Red stems, leaves broadly margined with white.

'Sibirica' Brilliant shiny red stems.

'Spaethii' A superb plant with red stems and strongly variegated golden foliage. Slightly less vigorous than the preceding cultivars.

C. stolonifera 'Flaviramea' With its yellow-green shoots, this is the perfect foil for the red-stemmed types.

FLOWERS

C. canadensis (Creeping Dogwood) H. 〒 ht: 6 in *15 cm* dist: 2 ft *60 cm* May-Jun, semi-shade. A dwarf suckering plant covered in summer with four-petalled white bracts sitting atop crowded groups of deeply veined leaves. Red tightly clustered fruits in autumn.

C. florida 'Rubra' Shr. ht: 9 ft *2.75 m* dist: 8-9 ft *2.5-2.75 m* May-Jun, full sun. The beautiful rose-pink notched bracts may be up to 4 in (10 cm) across, making this a very showy plant indeed. Couple this with good spring and autumn leaf coloration, and you have a good all-round garden plant. Several other cultivars are available. Prefers a neutral soil.

C. kousa chinensis Shr. to 〒 ht: 9 ft *2.75 m* dist: 8-9 ft *2.5-2.75 m* May-Jun, full sun. Rather similar to *florida* 'Rubra', but with white bracts and red strawberry-like fruits. Not a plant that thrives for everyone, but once seen in its full glory you will be tempted to try it. Prefers a neutral soil.

C. mas (Cornelian Cherry) Shr. ht: 9 ft *2.75 m* dist: 8-9 ft *2.5-2.75 m* Feb-Apr, full sun. If I had to choose just one *Cornus* it would be this one, for although it has neither the coloured bark nor large bracts of the other species, the clusters of tiny starry yellow flowers which crowd every bare twig in early spring are a joy to behold, and are extremely attractive to bees if the weather is at all kind. The broadly ovate leaves are heavily veined. There is in addition a golden-leafed form, 'Aurea', and an excellent variegated form, 'Variegata'. If you are lucky you may also see the bright red fruits which contrast nicely with the red-purple autumn leaf coloration. Easily grown on any soil, and completely hardy.

Corylus (Hazel, Cobnuts and Filberts) Pol. Shr. ψ
Feb-Mar, full sun, semi-shade
The wild nut tree or shrub is too rampant for the average garden, but there are some dwarf cultivars that will yield useful crops of nuts, so long as you are not in an area ranged over by squirrels. It is not a particularly decorative plant, but does have good yellow autumn colour. There are also some highly decorative forms that make excellent garden plants.

In all cases, male and female flowers are borne separately on the same plants. The lemon-yellow pendulous male catkins, in groups of 1-4, may be 2-3 in (5-7.5 cm) long and are a welcome sight on the hairy twigs in February and March, when they provide an easily accessible pollen source. The plant is wind pollinated and therefore, as with most wind-pollinated plants, the pollen has a low nutritive value. However, it is so early in the year that it is a useful source of fresh protein to the bees when the weather is suitable for collection. Unfortunately, in northern parts of Europe it is too cold in many years for the bees to forage on hazel catkins.

The female flowers appear as a cluster of red stigmas protruding only an ⅛ in (3 mm) or so from the ends of plump buds, and you will need to look closely to see these miniature sea-anemone-like structures. The nuts are too well known to need description, but the bracts surrounding them are invariably removed before they reach the shops. This is a pity, since they are very showy — strongly veined with 'frilled' edges. The further north one goes the smaller the nuts become, whilst in Mediterranean areas they are truly enormous by comparison.

C. avellana 'Pearson's Prolific' ht: 6-7 ft *2-2.25 m* dist: 6-7 ft *2-2.25 m* The least vigorous and therefore most suitable cultivar. Produces round nuts.

'Aurea' ht: 4-5 ft *1.25-1.5 m* dist: 4-5 ft *1.25-1.5 m* A yellow-green form that contrasts well with darker-foliaged plants. Rather slow growing.

'Contorta' ht: 8 ft *2.5 m* dist: 8 ft *2.5 m* Commonly known as 'Harry Lauder's Walking Stick', this curiously twisted yet highly ornamental plant is a delight when bedecked in catkins in early spring. The foliage is also distorted. Slow growing.

C. maxima 'Purpurea' ht: 15 ft *4.5 m* dist: 12-15 ft *3.5-4.5 m* The 'Purple Leaf Filbert' has very strong leaf coloration, and even the catkins, bracts and nuts take on some of the purple coloration.

Cotinus Nec. Shr.
Jun-Jul, full sun, shade
A truly marvellous genus of plants, with long-stalked, spoon-shaped leaves which are distinctly and pleasantly aromatic. Good red and/or gold autumn leaf colour (dependent on cultivar) is produced.

The four-petalled yellowish flowers, which are carried in loose pyramidal clusters, are tiny, less than ⅛ in (3 mm) in diameter. The whole inflorescence eventually lengthens and the long hairs on the flower stalks give a plume-like effect, earning the *Cotinus* its common name of Smoke Bush. Seed, incidentally, is rarely produced (unless warm weather prevails during the flowering period), most of the flowers falling off as soon as their colour fades.

C. coggygria ht: 10 ft *3 m* dist: 10-15 ft *3-4.5 m* Jun-Jul. The plain green form, all too rarely seen now — a great shame, because it is more showy, in a subtle way, than the purple forms, with its apple-green leaves and distinct seed heads which envelop the whole bush in a pink haze for many weeks in late summer and autumn. Golden autumn leaf coloration.

'Flame' ht: 10 ft *3 m* dist: 10-15 ft *3-4.5 m* Particularly fine orange-red leaf coloration in autumn.

'Notcutts Variety' ht: 6 ft *2 m* dist: 6 ft *2 m* Dark red leaves, the flowers taking on some of this coloration.

With all species, once they have reached the desired spread, the annual growth can be cut hard back in January. As well as keeping the bush neat and preventing it spoiling other plants, this will encourage freer flowering and larger leaves.

* Cotoneaster Nec/Pol Shr.
May-Jun, salt tol, full sun, shade
Well over a hundred different choices of this invaluable nectar-producing plant are available

Cotoneaster horizontalis, a plant probably more attractive to bees than any other in the garden.

to the beekeeper. To the honey bee these plants are some of the most attractive grown in gardens. Small or large, they mass on them, and on the large tree species the buzz can often be heard fifty yards away. The average nursery or garden centre, however, may stock only six or eight, which may range from a few inches high to those at 15 ft (4-5 m) plus.

The bulk of Cotoneasters are deciduous, but there are many which are evergreen. The flowers are mostly small — up to ½ in (1.3 cm) in diameter — and being white or pinkish are not usually regarded as showy, but beekeeper and gardener (and birds) alike will appreciate the colourful fruit (mostly red but sometimes yellow or black, depending on species or cultivar, about ¼ in (6 mm) in diameter) often plentifully produced in the autumn, and the brilliant red or copper autumn leaf colour of the deciduous kinds.These leaves may be retained, as with a beech hedge, until late winter in a sheltered spot.

Cotoneasters are susceptible to fire blight, a bacterial disease which can kill the entire plant, infection usually entering through the flowers. Many other rosaceous plants are also liable to attack. The disease decreases in prevalence as one travels from south to north in Europe, being most prevalent in southern France and Spain, although there have been recent reports of occurrences in northern Scotland. The disease is regarded as potentially so lethal that the British nursery industry is trying to introduce a voluntary ban to restrict the propagation of those species and cultivars of plants which are particularly susceptible. There are no suitable spray treatments. None of the species or cultivars listed here is likely to be included in the ban.

C. conspicuus 🐝 ◯ ht: 5 ft *1.5 m* dist: 3-4 ft *1-1.25 m* An evergreen shrub with small, up to ¼ in (6 mm), roundish, dark green leaves. The plant is variable in height and habit. Some forms are low and spreading, while others may be 6-8 ft (2-2.5 m), with arching branches. Try, if possible (if buying from a nursery that produces its own stock), to see the parent plant and ascertain if the plants being offered for sale have been propagated vegetatively or from

seed. Vegetatively propagated plants will retain the characteristics of the parent plant, whilst those from seed may well be very variable, particularly if other species or cultivars are grown in the vicinity and have been cross-pollinated by our bee friends!

The flowers have conspicuous dark red anthers. The fruit is shiny scarlet and is about ⅜ in (1 cm) across, and being relatively unattractive to birds is carried right through the winter.

C. dammeri 🐝 ≢ ht: 9-12 in *23-30 cm* dist: 2 ft *60 cm* A prostrate shrub ideal for covering banks in sun or shade, or as ground cover between other shrubs. Much more graceful of habit, with its slender creeping arched stems, than the stiff *horizontalis* types. The leaves are shiny, and on close inspection reveal an attractive net venation, reminiscent of many of the willows. W.J. Bean describes the fruits as being top-shaped, and this description perfectly fits the coral-red, freely produced fruits.

C. horizontalis ⅄ ≢ ht: 18 in *45 cm* dist: 3-4 ft *1-1.25 m* It is difficult to think of a more rewarding plant to grow: it seems to thrive on neglect and continues to flower profusely year after year — even on the poorest of soils, in sun or shade. Its normal horizontal growth habit can be reversed by planting it flat against a wall, so that its herring-bone shaped branches fan out over the wall instead of the soil; in this way it will happily reach 6 ft (2 m) or more with a minimum of support. It is a plant that the non-beekeeper may not want to go anywhere near on a sunny day, as the white flowers, pink on the outside, are invariably covered with bees. Small red fruits abundantly produced in the autumn hang on well into each new year (if the birds can be kept away), and then, in late autumn and winter, there is the added bonus of the small rounded leaves turning to red and then a burnished copper —delightful on even the dullest of winter days.

The more petite variegated form 'Variegatus', with its white-edged leaves which suffuse with pink when the first frosts arrive, is also well worth growing.

C. x 'Hybridus Pendulus' 🐝 🌳 ht: 5-6 ft

1.5-2 m dist: 6-7 ft *2-2.25 m* When grown on a 4-5 ft (1.2-1.5 m) stem (usually grafted on to *C. frigidus*), this must be the best small flowering and fruiting tree for the beekeeper's garden. The branches arch downwards under the weight of the brilliant red fruits, which contrast beautifully with the glossy leaves.

C. microphyllus 🌿 〒 ht: 3-4 ft *1-1.25 m* dist: 2-3 ft *60-90 cm* Small-leaved evergreen with stiff main branches and younger stems of dull red. The scarlet berries complement the leaves perfectly, and some that have escaped the birds can be found even in late winter, partially hidden as they are by the stiff short side shoots.

Due to its limited stature it is frequently seen clothing walls below ground-floor windows, for which — if kept in order by pruning and regular tying in — it is quite suitable.

'Cochleatus' A prostrate, slower-growing form with paler and broader leaves, this is a superb ·plant for the rock garden, alpine bed or dry wall. The dull red stems and leaf stalks make a stunning winter attraction, especially when complemented by the conspicuous scarlet fruit.

Crataegus (Quickthorn, May, Hawthorn)
Nec/Pol T. ☁ ⚬⚬
May-Jun, salt tol, full sun, semi-shade

The number of common names that a plant has will often reflect its distribution. The greater the number, the wider the spread, and the genus *Crataegus*, which has many local names, is very widely distributed throughout Europe, Asia and North America. A number of the species are known to produce ample pollen and nectar.

It is possibly one of the commonest and least fussy plants regarding soil and growing conditions that could be found; but for all that, whether it be for a hedge, specimen tree or shrub, if there is space then save a corner (just about anywhere will do) for a hawthorn. I rate them very highly as flowering trees because of the sheer mass of white or pink flower clusters that cover the entire tree in late spring, but remember that double flowers are useless to the bees, and as many of the cultivars of this plant are double, bees ignore them. On warm days the heady sweet smell of the flowers is blamed for many a headache, but the nectar flow is regarded as unreliable and unpredictable. Only about once in ten years or more does the flower produce a noticeable crop of honey, but when it does it is well worth waiting for as the honey has a delicious almond flavour. When nectar is present, it can be seen glistening as the numerous stamens open outwards in response to sunshine.

The flowers are followed in autumn by clusters of fruits, which in some species can be as large as crab apples, and just as showy. The leaves are lobed (sometimes almost to the mid-rib) or toothed and may colour well in autumn.

Hawthorns are susceptible to the disease fireblight, referred to in more detail under the genus *Cotoneaster*.

C. monogyna ht: 15 ft *4.5 m* The most familiar of the European hawthorns, far more common than *C. laevigata* (syn. *C. oxycantha*), from which it is not particularly distinct, except that it is thornier and more vigorous. The two species frequently hybridize in the wild. It has shining dark-red berries in autumn.

'Stricta' ht: 15 ft *4.5 m* If space is limited and an upright tree is wanted, then this relatively small specimen should be suitable.

C. laevigata 'Punicea' ht: 12-15 ft *3.5-4.5 m* Scarlet flowers.

'Rosea' ht: 12-15 ft *3.5-4.5 m* Pink flowers. Both this cultivar and 'Punicea' have small shiny dark-red berries in autumn.

C. x lavallei ht: 15-20 ft *4.5-6 m* The 2 in (5 cm) stout spines of this hybrid are vicious, but there are many compensations. The ovate leaves are 3-4 in (7.5-10 cm) long, toothed in part, and dark glossy green above, turning the most gorgeous rusty red-brown in autumn. These will persist regardless of hard frosts right through to Christmas, contrasting well with the 1 in (2.5 cm) ovoid fruits, which are a wonderful orange-brown and very persistent. The flowers are white and large in comparison with the other species and cultivars described above.

* **Crocus** Nec/Pol B/C.

ht: 6 in *15 cm* dist: 3-4 in *7-10 cm*
Feb-Apr, full sun

Although the crocus (along with the snowdrop) is often thought of as the earliest harbinger of spring, there are in fact many late autumn and winter-flowering species and cultivars, all of which are rich sources of pollen at a time when few others are available. However, those of most interest to the beekeeper are the spring-flowering types. These provide the honey bee with a large early source of high quality pollen as well as nectar. The bees are so eager to get at this wealth that they often force their way into the buds before the flowers are fully open — two or three bees, with large loads of bright orange pollen on their legs, all together in one flower, is a not uncommon sight in warm weather. Forage sources of this quality are of inestimable value to the bee colony at this time of population expansion and recovery from winter problems.

Additionally, there can be few more easily grown plants than the crocus, with such a superb range of flower colours, produced when most other plants are at their least interesting. Colours include white, blue, purple and yellow, with intermediate colours, bicolours and bronzing of the outside petals of many varieties. How many of us could resist buying the corms if they were available when the plants were in flower? Small quantities can in fact be bought in this way as pot plants, but this is a very expensive way of going about it. Buy them by the hundred if you can — even for a small garden — in autumn, and plant them in a sunny position about 2 in (5 cm) deep, and a rich reward will be yours in less than six months! The easiest way to plant into turf is to use a dibber (a broken fork handle sharpened is an ideal tool) or a bulb planter, and then just drop the corms in. Only the vigorous varieties (see below) are suitable for naturalizing in turf or amongst other prostrate plants. I grow vigorous yellow and blue varieties through *Polygonum affine* (another excellent bee plant) and this gives the bees a second harvest from the same piece of ground, from June to September. You will probably want to keep any grass short in the immediate vicinity of your hives, so do not be tempted to plant crocus, or any other bulbs, here, since the foliage should not be cut back until it has died off naturally (or the bulbs will be weakened), and this may not be before the end of June, by which time the grass will be pretty long.

Grow the less vigorous varieties on rock gardens, scree beds, and on the edge of borders. Keep other vigorous plants from encroaching on them.

C. chrysanthus This species contains more cultivars than any other and is deservedly widely planted. Between two and five flowers are produced from each corm, and this spreads the flowering period from mid-January to late March. None of the cultivars is vigorous enough for naturalizing.

'Blue Pearl' Pale silvery blue with orange stigma and a bronze base. Darker blue on the outside of the petals.

'Ladykiller' A striking colour combination: deep purple outside, edged with white, and white interior.

'Snow Bunting' Delicately scented, glistening white flowers with a golden throat and faint external purple feathering, orange stigma.

Seven or eight other *chrysanthus* cultivars are available in a range of colours from good bulb suppliers or garden centres.

C. tomasinianus Pale lavender-blue flowers in February, shaded silvery blue-grey on the outside. It grows strongly and is ideal (unlike its several cultivars) for naturalizing.

C. vernus Both this and its cultivars flower before the leaves are produced, and are two or three weeks later than the *chrysanthus* group. Often listed as 'large-flowered' or 'Dutch hybrids', the flowers are large and vulgar compared with, say, the delicacy of *Crocus* 'Snow Bunting'. Three to five flowers are produced per corm. They are, however, very showy and will compete strongly when naturalized in grass or low-growing plants. There is a wide colour range — blue, purple, white and yellow, with some cultivars, such as 'Pickwick', with stripes.

'Purpurea Grandiflora' A strong blue-purple.

The prolific Cytisus x praecox, a firm favourite with gardeners and bees.

'Joan of Arc' White with orange stigma.

'Golden Yellow Mammoth' The name describes it perfectly. There can be few more warming sights on a sunny spring day than coming unexpectedly upon a mass of these rich yellow flowers. The yellow cultivars are also popular with birds, which can destroy large numbers in their quest for nectar.

Cynoglossum (Hound's Tongue) Nec/Pol

full sun, semi-shade

The common name refers to the shape and texture of the leaves, which may vary from lance-shaped to ovate, with a rough hairy surface. The small blue or purplish flowers are produced in profusion, and are very similar in size and shape to those of the forget-me-not; they also have the same white eye, fringed with hairs, and a short corolla tube leading to the nectary.

C. amabile 'Firmament' A(h). ht: 18 in *45 cm* dist: 9 in *23 cm* Jun-Oct. The flowers are sky-blue, the foliage grey-green. Other named cultivars are also available.

C. nervosum H. ht: 2 ft *60 cm* dist: 18 in *45 cm* Jul-Aug. A superb plant with intense blue flowers on much-branched stems and long, narrow leaves.

C. officinale H. ht: 2½ ft *75 cm* dist: 18 in *45 cm* Jun-Aug. The wild Hound's Tongue is more interesting than pretty, its softly hairy grey leaves dominating the clusters of dull reddish-purple flowers. Certainly a plant that looks more at home in hedgerows and woodland than in a formal garden setting, but it does yield generous quantities of nectar.

* Cytisus (Broom) Nec/Pol Shr.

May-Jun, salt tol, full sun .

A very easily grown genus of plants, with a host of free-flowering species and cultivars with flowers as plain or bold as could be wished for. The brooms, particularly the smaller-flowered species, are worked very heavily by the honey bee for nectar and pollen, the latter being gathered in profusion and carried as large brownish-orange loads.

Many of the general details on cultivation, flowering and pruning given under the common broom (*scoparius*) apply equally to the other species and cultivars.

C. scoparius (Common Broom) ht: 6-7 ft *2-2.25 m* dist: 5-6 ft *1.5-2 m* A plant familiar to those who know little or nothing of gardening, since it is common in the wild, particularly on dry sandy soils in association with heather, gorse and honeysuckle, throughout much of Europe.

Every summer literally hundreds of gently arching, dark green whippy shoots are produced; these rarely exceed ⅛ in (3 mm) in diameter, but they may be up to 2 ft (60 cm) in

69

length. Every bud on these shoots will bear a golden yellow pea-like flower in the following late spring, turning the whole bush a gorgeous yellow from top to toe; and when a light breeze moves the flower-laden shoots and wafts the musky scent in your direction you will get an extra bonus.

The brown seed pods with their hard black seeds so freely borne are characteristic of all the brooms, and perhaps in this way they hope to compensate for the fact that they are not long-lived plants — 8-10 years is about as long as we can hope for. Trimming back the flowered shoots immediately after flowering helps to keep the plants vigorous. Use shears for the pruning, and if you cannot cut through the shoots you are attacking reasonably easily, you are attempting to cut back too far.

Brooms do have very small leaves, and you will not notice their passing; indeed, I always think of them as evergreens because they change so little over the winter.

C. scoparius has spawned a host of showy cultivars, many of which are bicolours, such as 'Andreanus' (yellow and crimson), and these really should be seen in flower before you purchase these rather harsh colour combinations.

C. albus syn. *multiflorus* ht: 8 ft *2.5 m* dist: 6-8 ft *2-2.5 m* The white Spanish Broom, free-flowering and a very good garden plant.

C. x beanii ht: 18 in *45 cm* dist: 18-24 in *45-60 cm* This is a really superb dwarf shrub with rich golden flowers.

C. x kewensis ht: 12 in *30 cm* dist: 2-3 ft *60-90 cm* Cream flowers, and another really good plant.

C. x praecox ht: 5 ft *1.5 m* dist: 5-6 ft *1.5-2 m* A particularly graceful and floriferous shrub, flowers the same colour as *x kewensis*.

'All Gold' ht: 4 ft *1.25 m* dist: 3-4 ft *1-1.25 m* Rather like a vigorous *x beanii*.

'Zeelandia' No doubt this multi-coloured cultivar will cause acute nausea to some, but I like its mixed lilac, cream and pink coloration.

Not all brooms flower in spring, and you might like to try *nigricans*, which grows to 4 ft (1.2 m) and has yellow flowers in late summer.

Daphne Nec/Pol Shr.

full sun

Medium to small evergreen or deciduous shrubs, often with marvellously fragrant terminal or axillary clusters of flowers ½ in (1.3 cm) across. The four almost flat petals, which may be of unequal size, lead to a short tube in which lie the 8-10 stamens. The petals of the flower are actually the calyx, there being no true petals. The flowers are attractive to bees, providing (particularly in the case of *D. mezereum*) the weather is warm and fine.

None of the daphnes takes kindly to being moved, so be sure to obtain container-grown plants.

D. x burkwoodii ht: 3 ft *1 m* dist: 2 ft *60 cm* May-Jun. Semi-evergreen with pale pink fragrant flowers crowding the branches in early summer.

D. cneorum (Garland Flower) ht: 6 in *15 cm* dist: 2 ft *60 cm* Apr-May. Wonderfully scented deep-pink flowers. This species is common in the mountains of Europe, where it sprawls over rocks quite happily with dwarf gorse and grass.

D. collina ht: 1 ft *30 cm* dist: 1 ft *30 cm* May. Dark green leaves, fragrant rose-purple flowers. A rather slow grower.

D. mezereum ht: 4 ft *1.25 m* dist: 3 ft *1 m* Feb-Mar. When it flowers well — which it refuses to do for me whilst it thrives in certain other (neglected) gardens — there are few more rewarding plants to grow. The bright pink flowers, with their sequin-like surface and sweet fragrance, have to be the best thing to be found in the garden in February. A white form, 'Alba', is also very attractive. It does well on neutral soils, but will thrive even in limey ones. Birds, particularly finches, can decimate the flower buds of this and other species before they even open out, and they are also responsible for removing the berries before they give any semblance of a display.

D. retusa ht: 18 in *45 cm* dist: 12-18 in *30-45 cm* May-Jun. A rather stiff slow-growing shrub with white fragrant flowers, tinged with purple.

Deutzia scabra

Deutzia Pol. Shr. ⚥ ☁
Jun-Jul, full sun, semi-shade
It is difficult to explain why these most elegant free-flowering shrubs are not more commonly seen in gardens, whilst their close relative, *Philadelphus*, has enjoyed much greater favour. The five-petalled, star-like flowers, 1 in (2.5 cm) in diameter, are really quite beautiful, usually pink on the outside and white within, and carried in loosely branched clusters. The ten stamens are like narrow petals and are forked towards the tip, with the yellow anther sitting in the fork. The three pistils are held well above the 'crown' of stamens.

D. x elegantissima 'Fasciculata' ht: 5 ft *1.5 m* dist: 5 ft *1.5 m* Jun. Fragrant bright rose-pink flowers.

D. x hybrida 'Perle Rose' ht: 6 ft *2 m* dist: 6 ft *2 m* Pale rose flowers.

D. x kalmiiflora ht: 4 ft *1.25 m* dist: 4 ft *1.25 m* Jun. Large pale carmine flowers.

D. monbeigii ht: 5 ft *1.5 m* dist: 5 ft *1.5 m* Jun. Glistening white flowers, and small leaves which are white beneath.

D. x rosea ht: 3 ft *1 m* dist: 3 ft *1 m* Jun. There are several cultivars of this most graceful species, with white, rose or pink flowers. The cultivar 'Grandiflora', with its large white flowers suffused with pink, is particularly showy.

D. scabra ht: 10 ft *3 m* dist: 8 ft *2.5 m* Jun-Jul. A rather upright species producing large clusters of erect, white, bell-shaped flowers which are often suffused with pink.

71

Dianthus

The pinks and carnations are wonderful garden plants, with their waxy, grey-green narrow leaves and brilliant single flowers, often most gloriously fragrant. I grow several species, none of which, unfortunately, is of any great interest to the honey bee, the nectar being inaccessible at the bottom of the long flower tubes.

D. barbatus (Sweet William) Nec. Bien. 🌿 Jun-Jul, full sun. This is perhaps the best species to grow for honey bees. The domed flower heads, 4-5 in (10-12.5 cm) across, are made up of many individual flowers 1 inch (2.5 cm) or so across, and can be obtained in a wide variety of colours from white through to dark red. Zonal flower markings in contrasting colours are an attractive feature of many of the plants, and the clove-like fragrance is a delight. Dwarf strains as low as 4 in (10 cm) are available. Seed should be sown in June for flowering the following summer. Do not expect a longer life span from your plants than 2-3 years.

Leopard's bane, Doronicum plantagineum, makes a good show just as the daffodils are finishing and, as with all composite flowers, is popular with honey bees.

* **Doronicum** (Leopard's Bane) Nec/Pol H. 🌿
Mar-May, full sun, semi-shade
Large, bright yellow flowers, as early as April, make *Doronicum* (in one of its forms), a must for the gardener and beekeeper alike. Although the daisy-like flowers are single, the petals are numerous and radiate from the domed centre, with its hundreds of individual florets. The long outer petals are well supported from beneath by 2-3 rows of sharply pointed bracts. *Doronicum* does well in any soil, and they are vigorous growers. The early-flowering species are most useful to the beekeeper.

D. caucasicum ht: 18 in *45 cm* dist: 12 in *30 cm*
Solitary yellow flowers 2 in (5 cm) across.

D. x 'Miss Mason' ht: 2 ft *60 cm* dist: 18 in *45 cm*
Pale yellow flowers 3 in (7.5 cm) across.

D. plantagineum 'Harpur Crewe' ht: 3 ft *1 m* dist: 2 ft *60 cm* Golden yellow flowers 3-4 in (7.5-10 cm) across.

There is one other plant I cannot resist mentioning here, which although it is not a *Doronicum* is very similar, as indicated by the name *Senecio doronicum* (and also appreciated by the honey bee). I collected seed of this variable yellow-golden 'Doronicum' from the alpine meadows of the Maritime Alps, and have grown it for years in a shallow 5 in (12.5 cm) bed of soil lain directly on concrete, and it thrives! The flowering period is later: Jun-Aug.

All the doronicums make excellent bee plants and cut flowers.

Echinops (Globe Thistle) Nec. H. ♠
Jul-Sep, full sun

This is one of those plants that is so easy to grow that it never seems to get any special attention. In the long term this has earned it a reputation as a rather ordinary untidy plant, which, if it is given a little care, it most certainly ·is not. Handsome and distinctive is a more apposite description.

The spherical flowers, 2-3 in (5-7.5 cm) across, are packed with literally hundreds of small, star-like, narrowly lobed florets. The short floret tubes provide easy bee access, and sit atop a spiny cluster of bracts. These give the flower head a certain firmness, but they do not detract from its appearance as they are largely hidden by the floret petals. The bulk of the flower heads are carried at the end of long, erect stalks, and contrast well with the white woolly stems and thistle-like leaves, green above and grey beneath.

Even when the garden is full of flowers in July and August, *Echinops* are sought out by honey bees, and in spite of some reports that the nectar has a narcotic effect on them, this is not a side effect that I have personally ever noticed. Bumble bees are, however, often heavily affected. They will often be seen, two or three at a time, sitting still on the flower head and if tapped on the back with the finger appear to just hunch up a little, or put up a leg to ward you off. It has been suggested that as they sup up a much greater volume of nectar than the

honey bee, they pick up sufficient of the narcotizing substance to immobilize them for a while.

E. humilis ht: 5 ft *1.5 m* dist: 3-4 ft *1-1.25 m* Leaves less spiny than in many species, flowers steely blue.

'Taplow Blue' ht: 6 ft *2 m* dist: 4 ft *1.25 m* Flowers pale blue.

E. ritro 'Veitch's Blue' ht: 3 ft *1 m* dist: 18-24 in *45-60 cm* Dark blue flowers.

Echium Nec/Pol A(h). ♠
ht: 12 in *30 cm* dist: 9 in *23 cm*
Jun-Oct, full sun

These plants are very attractive to bees, providing both nectar and pollen in good quantity, but unfortunately are rarely in sufficient quantity to provide a surplus of honey.

E. vulgare (Viper's Bugloss) This plant is widespread in Europe and parts of Asia, and has been naturalized into North America. It thrives naturally on dry sandy soils and is an early colonizer of old gravel pits. The central stem and the narrow leaves are covered with stiff hairs, giving the whole plant a very rough feel. The stems are also speckled, hence the unusual common name. The 1 in (2.5 cm) flowers are carried in a line on lateral stems, which are at first coiled up but extend as the buds develop and bloom. The buds are pink, but gradually change to a bright blue funnel-shaped flower when fully open, with five protruding blue stamens carried on pink filaments. The pollen is blue as well. With a number of these uncoiling stems of bloom above each other, the whole effect is magnificent. The plant is really a biennial, but is usually treated as an annual in the garden.

E. lycopsis syn. *plantagineum* (Purple Viper's Bugloss) This plant is more restricted in its natural form, being local to the Mediterranean region, and the Channel Islands and Cornwall in Britain, although it does turn up in other areas as a garden escape. It was naturalized into Australia, where it became a major arable weed and earned the name of 'Patterson's Curse'. It was more popular amongst the beekeepers. It is very similar to *E. vulgare* but is much softer to the touch, and the flowers, densely bunched on much longer side stems, start red in colour and turn purple-blue. Thanks to the efforts of the plant breeders the colour range has been widened to include white, pale blue and pink, and this has ensured its presence in many more gardens than previously. Sow seeds in situ during September or March-April, in drills 9 in (23 cm) apart.

'Blue Bedder' Deep purple flowers.

'Dwarf Hybrids' Purple, blue, pink and white flowers.

Eranthis (Winter Aconite) Nec/Pol B/C
ht: 3-6 in *7.5-15 cm* dist: 3-4 in *7.5-10 cm*
Jan-Feb, full sun, semi-shade
An irresistible plant that associates well with snowdrops and spring-flowering cyclamen.

The solitary 1 in (2.5 cm) cup-shaped flowers, with their 6-8 rounded petals, are very similar in colour and texture to the buttercups, and are a joy to behold so early in the new year, especially so for any bees that happen to be around, for the protected inner row of 'petals' is adapted into notched spoon-shaped nectaries, each glistening with nectar even on dull cold days. The branched anthers carry generous pollen loads, making this a very valuable bee plant. Beneath the flower is a much-divided leafy bract with twenty or so finger-like projections. These are a feature of all species and cultivars, but are more pronounced in some than others.

Although they grow well enough in light soils, top dressing with leaf mould or peat will help to strengthen your 'colonies', for no one should plant less than a hundred of them — they can easily be fitted into an area of no more than three feet square. Plant them 2-3 in (5-7.5 cm) deep, and as early in autumn as you can obtain them.

E. cilicicus Similar to *hyemalis* but less invasive, and the flowers are a deeper yellow.

The vivid yellow Eranthus hyemalis, or winter aconite, is one of the very earliest bee flowers to bloom each year.

E. hyemalis Probably the most popular species due to the ease of its cultivation. It will compete quite happily with snowdrops and crocuses.

E. x tubergineana 'Guinea Gold' Flowers large; often regarded as the best of the bunch.

* **Erica** (Heaths) Nec/Pol Shr. 🐝 ☁
full sun, semi-shade

The ericas or heaths are closely related to the callunas, and superficially bear them a close resemblance, but botanically they are quite distinct. There is a wide range of species with very different soil requirements (they do not all require acid soils) and growth habits, a small selection of which are described below. Honey bees work these plants avidly for both nectar and pollen. The honey produced from the ericas is not classed as heather honey: this comes from the callunas. Erica honey is a normal fluid, not a jelly, port wine in colour and very strong and bitter in taste.

Most of the individual species and cultivars will flower for around two months, depending on the weather, so although the flowering period shown against each species may cover several months, do not expect nectar and pollen from your one cultivar to cover this whole period! The individual flowers are usually carried in terminal clusters and vary in shape from bell to flask to cylinder. The calyx is far less prominent than that of ling, and is made up of four pointed sepals which are the same colour as the flower tube, spreading outwards as the flower opens.

If you wish to control the size of your plants then clip them over with shears immediately after flowering, with the exception of *E. australis*. I prefer to do this only one year in four or five, since the old flower spikes are very attractive. The *vagans* cultivars are outstanding in this respect. Armed with a knowledge of your own soil conditions and required flowering periods, take a trip to a good park or garden to see the mature plants before making any purchases, because although they may all sound rather similar they do look very different in the flesh.

E. australis ht: 4 ft *1.25 m* dist: 3-4 ft *1-1.25 m* Apr-May, acid. The Spanish heath is a plant

Erica x darleyensis, a small spreading shrub with rosy-purple flowers. An erica bed in a garden will give warm colour and flowers for the bees over a long period.

that is unfortunately not seen very often in cultivation in more northern areas, perhaps because it is not reliably hardy in all districts. However, I have seen these beautiful 4-6 ft (1.25-2 m) plants growing in cold parts of Britain, literally smothered with flowers, looking just like pink or white clouds year after year. Fragrant.

'Mr Robert' White flowers.

'Riverslea' Red-purple flowers.

E. cinerea (Bell Heather) ht: 12 in *30 cm* dist: 12 in *30 cm* Jun-Oct, acid. The native bell heather is commonly found growing in association with callunas on heathland and moors. Its short rounded flowers make for easy bee access and are carried along the whole length of the young shoots.

'Atrorubens' Long spikes of brilliant red flowers.

'C.D.Eason' Very dark green foliage with pink flowers.

'Pink Ice' Again, dark green foliage with vivid pink flowers. This has to be one of the best heaths in cultivation.

E. x darleyensis ht: 18 in *45 cm* dist: 18 in *45 cm* Nov-Apr. Slightly larger and more spreading than *E. herbacea*, with which it is often associated. The individual flowers are often longer too, and this enhances the effect of the protruding dark brown anthers. Lime tolerant.

'George Rendall' Flowers deep glowing pink, carried over a long period.

'Silberschmelze' A really marvellous white-flowered hybrid with dark foliage and scented flowers.

E. herbacea syn. *carnea* (Winter Heath) ht: 12-18 in *30-45 cm* dist: 12-18 in *30-45 cm* Dec-Apr. Its winter flowering, tolerance of alkaline soils and ease of cultivation have made this a very popular species with the whole gardening fraternity, and beds of them — often combined with dwarf conifers — appear everywhere. This is fortuitous for the beekeeper, since the early spring-flowering forms are very popular with, and helpful to, honey bees.

'Atrorubra' Deep pink flowers.

'Aurea' The foliage is golden in spring and summer, but bright coppery-red over winter, and this acts as a perfect foil for the pale pink flowers which are freely produced in February. Definitely one of the best of a very large number of cultivars.

'December Red' Dark foliage with showy magenta pink flowers.

'Foxhollow Fairy' A most unusual cultivar with dark vibrant magenta sepals. The flower tube is white at first but gradually takes on the same colour as the sepals. The protruding brown anthers give the final touch to a very attractive dark-green-foliaged plant.

'Springwood Pink' Trailing shoots with rose-pink flowers.

'Springwood White' A vigorous free-flowering cultivar producing numerous long trailing shoots packed with flowers.

'Vivellii' Very dark foliage turning bronzy-red in winter. The flowers are a vivid carmine. A very showy plant. Rather more difficult to propagate than many other cultivars, so you may need to hunt for it and perhaps pay a little extra when you find it!

E. mediterranea syn. *erigena* ht: 3 ft *1 m* dist: 2 ft *60 cm* Mar-May. This species has an erect growth habit, and the urn-shaped flowers are fragrant. Lime tolerant.

'Brightness' The bronze-red flower buds open to a rose-pink.

'Superba' ht: 6 ft *2 m* dist: 4 ft *1.25 m* Pink flowers.

'W.T.Rackliffe' ht: 3 ft *1 m* dist: 2 ft *60 cm* Similar habit to 'Brightness'. The white flowers have protruding brown anthers, and these look fine against the dark green foliage.

E. tetralix ht: 12-18 in *30-45 cm* dist: 12 in *30 cm* Jun-Oct, acid. The leaves of this species, native to Britain and western Europe, are arranged in fours, forming a cross, giving this plant its common name — 'the cross-leaved heath'. The leaves are small, dark green above, pale grey beneath, the margins of which are folded inwards and covered with short stiff hairs. The flowers, ¼-⅓ in (6-8 mm) long, carried in terminal clusters, are urn-shaped and almost closed at the ends. At the 'mouth' the petals fold back slightly to form a small four-pointed collar. The shiny brown stigma extends beyond the collar, looking just like a too-long bell clapper.

'Alba Mollis' Small, distinctly grey leaves, white flowers.

'Alba Praecox' White flowers with grey foliage.

'Con Underwood' Crimson flowers with greyish-green foliage.

'L.E.Underwood' Silver-grey foliage with terra-cotta buds turning to pale pink.

E. vagans ht: 12-18 in *30-45 cm* dist: 12 in *30 cm* Jul-Oct, acid. The aptly named Cornish Heath may be found growing wild in abundance on the Lizard peninsula. The leaves are needle-like and are carried in whorls of 4 or 5. The flowers are densely packed together, making this a very showy species. The small upward-pointing bell-shaped flowers are carried on fine long stalks, and the brown-tipped stamens add a distinct and pretty touch to the flowers, since they always exceed them in length. There is usually new growth of 1 in (2.5 cm) or so above the top of the flower spikes. Most cultivars will grow to about 18-24 in (45-60 cm), and although the colour range of *vagans* is narrow, it is not a plant I would want to be without. If you have the space and your soil is not alkaline, then you must grow at least two of the cultivars listed below.

'Fiddlestone' Rose-pink flowers.

'Lyonesse' Pure white flowers, which remain an attractive brown throughout the winter period.

'Mrs D.F.Maxwell' Deep cerise pink.

'White Rocket' Fully 6 in (15 cm) flower spikes; fewer plants could be more aptly named. A magnificent plant.

Eryngium Nec. H. 🌱

Jul-Sep, salt tol, full sun
Striking foliage plants with spiny narrow leaves. The flowers of all species are surrounded by a ruff of toothed lance-shaped bracts, frequently the same colour as the flowers. The individual flowers are tiny but are packed together in dense conical heads. The whole plant appears to have a most distinctive metallic finish. With all species, try to avoid root disturbance.

E. alpinum ht: 2 ft *60 cm* dist: 18 in *45 cm* Large blue flowers.

E. amethystinum ht: 2 ft *60 cm* dist: 18 in *45 cm* Smaller flowers than *alpinum*, but darker blue.

E. x oliveranum ht: 3 ft *1 m* dist: 2 ft *60 cm* Green leaves and blue flowers, soft to the touch.

E. proteiflorum ht: 3 ft *1 m* dist: 2 ft *60 cm* Flower head almost egg-shaped, 2 in (5 cm) long. The ruff of bracts are wider, longer and palish green against a darker green foliage.

Escallonia Nec/Pol Shr. 🌿

salt tol, full sun
A handsome, easily grown and free-flowering shrub, available in a range of white, pink and red-flowered forms and in sizes to suit even the smallest garden. To my mind escallonias are very under-rated as garden plants and, being such copious producers of nectar, they are well worth a place in any beekeeper's garden.

The small glossy leaves are finely toothed, and during a normal winter will be retained. During severe winters, such as that of 1984 in Britain, every leaf may be lost and new ones may not appear until June, perhaps 2-3 ft (60-90 cm) back from the tips. The dead parts should be cut away, and by the end of the summer it should be difficult to see that any damage had occurred. However, to obtain the best display in colder districts some shelter from wind and frosts is very desirable.

The flowers have five rounded petals (with a short tubular base where the nectar collects), usually no more than ½ in (1.3 cm) wide. They are carried in terminal and axillary clusters. An outstanding plant for seaside areas in particular.

E. x rigida 'Donard Radiance' ⬭ ht: 4 ft *1.25 m* dist: 4 ft *1.25 m* May-Oct. Showy, large rose-red flowers. Very hardy.

'Appleblossom' ⬭ ht: 5 ft *1.5 m* dist: 5 ft *1.5 m* May-Oct. Aptly named, the pink buds opening to white. A very attractive plant.

'Edinensis' ⬭ ht: 7 ft *2.25 m* dist: 7 ft *2.25 m* May-Oct. Graceful arching habit, flowers bright pink. Very hardy.

'Iveyi' ⬭ ht: 8 ft *2.5 m* dist: 8 ft *2.5 m* Aug-Oct. A vigorous plant with the largest leaves of those listed here, and large clusters of white flowers. Very hardy.

'Langleyensis' ⬭ ht: 7 ft *2.25 m* dist: 7 ft *2.25 m* May-Oct. Arching habit, with deep rose-pink flowers. Very hardy.

E. rubra 'Woodside' ⚏ ht: 18 in *45 cm* dist: 3 ft *1 m* Jul-Oct. Rather spreading habit. The flowers are crimson and, though small, very freely carried.

Eschscholzia Nec/Pol A(h). 𝕛

Jun-Oct, dry, salt tol, full sun, semi-shade
Like most poppies, *Eschscholzia* is a real sun
lover. The flowers remain closed in dull light
but open increasingly to saucer stage, depending
on the intensity of sunlight.

The colour range is wide and vibrant, and the
petals, often fluted in the new hybrids, have the
most wonderful satiny texture that, like the
buttercup, reflects the sunlight. A lovely sight
on a sunny day, with the extra delight of a few
bees taking home loads of yellow pollen.

The fern-like foliage is greeny-grey and is
attractive in its own right, but it is also an
excellent foil for the flowers. Sow in situ.

E. californica (Californian Poppy) ht: 12-18 in *30-
45 cm* dist: 9 in *23 cm* Yellow flowers. The species
is rarely grown now, but many excellent
hybrids have been raised from it.

'Ballerina' Flowers mostly single, up to 2½ in
(6.5 cm) in diameter, with some semi-doubles,
colours ranging through the reds, oranges,
yellows to white. Rarely exceeds a foot (30 cm)
in height.

E. caespitosa ht: 6 in *15 cm* dist: 9 in *23 cm*
Altogether a more dainty plant in flower and
foliage. The single flowers are lemon-yellow,
up to 1 in (2.5 cm) in diameter, making it very
suitable for edging or rock gardens. Sometimes
sold under the name of Primrose or Miniature
Primrose, and though these may be more
attractive names than *caespitosa*, they are not
valid.

* Eucryphia Nec/Pol Shr. 𝕛

full sun, semi-shade
Another of those marvellous plants that, once
seen in full flower, you just have to persist in
trying to grow, even though it is not always
reliably hardy, except in milder and coastal
areas, or where very well sheltered from cold
winds by a wall or other plants. In such
locations it will, once well established, thrive
and survive severe winters: there is one such
superb flourishing specimen, well over 30 ft (9
m) high, in the gardens of a National Trust
property in eastern Scotland, which is about ten

miles inland, well north of the Forth estuary.

The waxy pure-white flowers, carried singly
or in pairs, may be over 2 in (5 cm) in diameter,
and are packed with masses of orange or
yellow-tipped stamens, which produce abundant pollen over a very long period. The
toothed, deep-green shiny leaves are rather
leathery, usually with 3-5 leaflets.

All *Eucryphia* prefer lime-free soil, but can
tolerate a degree of alkalinity as long as the
organic content of the soil is high.

Try to plant out your container-grown plants
after all frosts have gone, and plant other
expendable shrubs close to them to give some
measure of protection during the winter. Cut
these back to prevent over-crowding as necessary.

E. glutinosa 𝖸 ht: 12-15 ft *3.5-4.5 m* dist: 8-10 ft
2.5-3 m Jul-Aug, full sun. A towering column of
white flowers during the summer, with the
added bonus of good autumn leaf colour.

E. nymansensis 'Nymansay' 🌿 ht: 20 ft *6 m* dist:
12-15 ft *3.5-4.5 m* Aug-Sep. Fuller, overlapping
petals. Very free flowering.

The bees work these hypericum-like flowers for
both nectar and pollen, and on warm days
there can be one or two bees in every flower.
This pollen is particularly valuable to bees,
because they will be collecting their winter store
of protein and will be feeding up to lay down
body stores of fat and protein for the dearth
period of winter.

Filipendula Pol. H. ☁

wet, semi-shade
The Meadowsweet (*F. ulmaria*), native throughout Europe, thrives in damp marshy places and
produces rather feathery lop-sided spikes
packed with small cream flowers, which attract
bees in large numbers, many of which will be
collecting delicate lime-green loads of pollen
often mistaken by beekeepers as the pollen
from lime trees. In spite of the sweet smell,
nectar is not usually produced in quantity in
Britain, although bees do work the plant for
nectar in other areas of Europe. Unless you
have a marshy area in your garden you would
be unlikely to want to introduce the Meadow-

sweet to a garden setting. Heavy annual mulches can do much to make the other filipendulas listed more suitable for non-marshy areas.

F. kamtschatica 'Elegantissima Rosea' ht: 4 ft *1.25 m* dist: 2-3 ft *60-90 cm* Jun-Aug. Glistening satin-pink flowers.

F. multijuga syn. *palmata* ht: 3 ft *1 m* dist: 2 ft *60 cm* Jun-Jul. Pink flowers.

F. vulgaris syn. *hexapetala* 'Grandiflora' (Drop-wort) ht: 3 ft *1 m* dist: 18-24 in *45-60 cm* Jun-Jul. Creamy-white flower spikes and fine carrot-like foliage. Unlike other species this will also thrive in dry (normal) soils.

Forsythia (Golden Bell Flower) Nec/Pol Shr.
Mar-Apr, full sun, semi-shade

There can be few shrubs that grow and flower so easily and profusely as the forsythia, as evidenced by a trip through suburbia in spring — nearly every garden has at least one bush, which will invariably be covered from top to toe in a mass of flowers. I would hate to be without forsythia in my own garden, for, flowering early as they do, they brighten the scene when very few other plants are in flower, and perhaps more importantly they can provide a valuable early nectar and pollen source.

The nodding yellow flowers are shallowly bell-shaped, up to 1½ in (3.5 cm) across, with four petals, and are carried in clusters, usually on short spurs before the leaves are produced. The young shoots and spurs are green-brown. The leaves can be up to 4 in (10 cm) in length, and vary in width; they may be shallowly or deeply toothed towards the tip. The plant's general habit is rather open, but with a tendency towards erect growth, particularly when cut back in order to contain them, as with hedges, and this treatment has, in fact, the reverse effect from that desired, encouraging even more vigorous upright shoots with few flowers to be produced.

In some years flowering may be disappointing, particularly following a severe winter. This is usually the result of birds taking the plump flower buds for food; some black cotton draped over the bushes will help to prevent this loss being too great.

F. x intermedia 'Beatrix Farrand' ht: 11 ft *3.25 m* dist: 8 ft *2.5 m* Free-flowering and with the largest flowers, of deep canary yellow. The throat is a darker yellow-orange and the leaves are very deeply toothed.

'Spectabilis' ht: 9 ft *2.75 m* dist: 6 ft *2 m* A superb free-flowering shrub slightly less vigorous than 'Beatrix Farrand'.

F. ovata ht: 5 ft *1.5 m* dist: 4 ft *1.25 m* This species has deeper yellow, smaller, but much more broadly petalled flowers than the preceding cultivars, and is an ideal choice for the smaller garden.

Fuchsia Nec/Pol H/Shr.
salt tol, full sun, semi-shade

The graceful pendulous *Fuchsia* flowers have a waxy beauty all their own. The upper part of the flower is tubular (long or short depending on variety), and from this narrow 'waist' the petals flare out to give a hooped-petticoat effect. Those types with double flowers — multiple petticoats, as it were — are of less interest, since although they do yield pollen, nectar access for the honey bee is rather restricted. This problem is even greater in varieties with long, narrow upper flower tubes, such as *F. thalia*. The outer 'petals' (actually sepals) are frequently in contrasting colours to the inner ones, from which they fold back. The crowning touch is the long protruding pistil surrounded by a mass of stamens which together almost double the length of the flower. An exquisite plant.

The fuchsias listed are hardy enough to become shrubs (with stems that persist through the winter) in the milder southwest and coastal districts of Britain. They are, however, capable of re-generating from the root-stock in colder areas, provided some protection is given to the crown of the plant; this can be done either with a cloche or coarsely sieved peat.

F. magellanica 'Gracilis Tricolour' ht: 3 ft *1 m* dist: 3 ft *1 m* Graceful arching branches, and dainty leaves margined with creamy-yellow, flushed pink and grey. Flowers small, with red sepals and purple petals. Slightly less hardy than the species.

'Mrs Popple' ht: 3 ft *1 m* dist: 2 ft *60 cm* Large flowers with red sepals and purple petals.

'Riccartonii' ht: 4 ft *1.25 m* dist: 3 ft *1 m* Graceful arching branches packed with small flowers with crimson sepals and purple petals.

All the more exotic 'pot-plant' fuchsias will also grow well enough out of doors for the summer in cool temperate areas. Try bedding a few out in a sunny spot in June.

Nectar production is obviously greater in sunny locations and districts, where the flowers may be worked with some enthusiasm by honey bees, but fuchsias will also thrive in semi-shade. This semi-shade can take the form of a low wall or other plants, and this will help to minimize winter plant losses.

* **Gaillardia** (Blanket Flower) Nec/Pol H.

Jun-Nov, full sun

An unendearing common name for another member of the huge Compositae family, of which the bees are so fond. *Gaillardia* stands out because it flowers for such a very long period, and will grow just about anywhere if it has full sun. The flowers are typically daisy-like, with several rows of ray florets. In most cultivars the florets are tipped with yellow or pale orange, the ground colour being red or red-brown. All are natives of central and southern USA, where in some areas they are important bee plants.

Perennial types can be propagated by division or root cuttings, and to retain their vigour they should be cut down to a few inches, and watered and fed before the first frosts. The annual types, of which several are available, can be raised from seed, which may be sown in situ in March/April.

G. aristata 'Croftway Yellow' ht: 2 ft *60 cm* dist: 18 in *45 cm* Florets all yellow, centre yellow-orange.

'Dazzler' ht: 2 ft *60 cm* dist: 18 in *45 cm* Orange tips, red centre.

'Goblin' ht: 9 in *23 cm* dist: 9 in *23 cm* Yellow tips, red-brown centre. One of the most

commonly seen herbaceous plants, which as well as all its other attributes makes an excellent cut flower.

G. pulchella ht: 15 in *40 cm* dist: 12 in *30 cm* Mostly red-purple florets, otherwise similar to *aristata*, with which it has been hybridized to produce a range of variously coloured hybrids.

* **Galanthus** Nec/Pol
ht: 6-8 in *15-18 cm* dist: 3-4 in *7.5-10 cm*
Jan-Apr, semi-shade, shade
How well both the British and French common names, 'Snowdrop' and 'Perce Neige', fit this hardy dwarf bulb. Cool shady growing conditions such as can be found beneath trees, where the soil may be bone dry in summer, suit the snowdrop very well. Given these conditions the clumps will expand at such a rate, even on a light sandy soil, that if they were not so welcome they might be thought invasive.

The flowering season is long — several weeks — and this would appear to be essential to ensure pollination in January, February and March. The buds are held erect at first, but later 'drop' as they break free of the enveloping sheath. The outer three petals, pure white, spread widely like a propellor, perhaps 1½ in (3.5 cm) across, to reveal the short ½ in (1.3 cm) inner petals. These overlap and each is conspicuously but shallowly notched at the centre. Apple-green markings on both the inside and outside of the white inner petals vary with species and cultivar. The six anthers, like miniature spears, bear bright yellow/orange pollen. To me, the scented forms smell of honey.

In suitable weather, bees will work snowdrops very heavily. It is an early source of valuable good-quality pollen, which will be seen as rather shiny yellow-brown loads on the legs of most of the foragers.

The temptation to mix snowdrops with other colourful spring-flowering bulbs such as the winter aconites and scillas is too much for most people. They do not seem to care too much for 'punk' on the streets, but are more than happy to encourage it in their own gardens!

Few people succeed in establishing snowdrops when they purchase dry bulbs. Snow-

The vivid blue of Gentiana verna, a colour rarely approached by other plants.

drops are in fact one of the few bulbs that move best when green (that is, immediately after flowering). They are rarely offered for sale green, so try to beg a few clumps from a neighbour at the appropriate time — perhaps in exchange for a jar of honey. Plant them 4 in (10 cm) deep.

G. elwesii A variable species with relatively broad glaucous leaves. The inner petals each have two green spots which in some forms merge. The thick stems bear large egg-shaped flowers.

G. ikariae This species is easily distinguished by its shiny dark green leaves. The inner petals are distinctly notched and have pale green markings. Scented.

G. nivalis The common snowdrop, and naturalized in many areas. The flower stems are sturdy — rarely exceeding 8 in (20 cm), and the markings on the inner petals are dark green. Scented.

Leucojum, or spring snowflake, are similar to, but rather larger than, the snowdrop and more

The vivid blue of Gentiana verna, a colour rarely approached by other plants.

showy, and are preferred by some. They are not as widely grown as snowdrops, but do yield good early pollen and some nectar.

Gentiana (Gentian) Nec/Pol
The very name Gentian evokes the clean freshness of the Alps, and of course the bright and variable blues of the flowers are stunning, although there are in fact other colours, including yellow and white.

Now do not stop reading just because your soil is not acid or is heavy: gentians are as variable in their soil requirements as they are in their growth habits and flower coloration — a species (or one of its many hybrids) can be found to suit most conditions. One thing they do not like is waterlogged soil or poor drainage.

Most species have a tufted carpeting growth habit, with opposite pairs of grass-like leaves arranged alternately. The blue chalice-shaped flowers, variously striped and/or spotted, flare outwards into five rounded or pointed petals. Although the stems may be rather lax, the flowers are held erect, and this ensures that the ¼ in (6 mm) or so of nectar at the flower base is conserved for bees or other insects.

The dwarf species are ideal for the rock garden, scree or terrace.

G. acaulis (Trumpet or Bell Gentian) H. ht: 6-9 in *15-23 cm* dist: 6-9 in *15-23 cm* Jun-Jul, full sun, semi shade. Deep blue solitary flowers up to 2 in (5 cm) long and 1 in (2.5 cm) across, the throat spotted green and striped. Reputed to be rather fickle about producing flowers, but does well in my own garden without any special attention.

G. asclepiadea (Willow Gentian) H. ht: 2 ft *60 cm* dist: 12 in *30 cm* Jul-Sep, semi-shade. A most beautiful and floriferous species with deep blue flowers with paler stripes carried on graceful leafy stems. Once established, do not disturb the clumps.

G. farreri H. ht: 6 in *15 cm* dist: 6 in *15 cm* Sep-Oct. Showy 'Cambridge' blue flowers, spotted with greenish blue, terminal and solitary, on decumbent stems. Tolerant of some lime in the soil.

G. septemfida H. ht: 6-9 in *15-23 cm* dist: 6-9 in *15-23 cm* Aug-Sep, full sun, semi-shade. Perhaps the easiest and most reliable species, thriving in almost any reasonable situation, where it will form large clumps with the usual trailing stems. Flowers up to 1 in (2.5 cm) or so long, carried in clusters of seven or so, purplish blue with markings on the inside of the petals disappearing into the paler throat. Also distinctive are the very finely branched secondary 'petals' between the larger petals, giving it the look of a gentianella rather than a gentian.

G. sino-ornata H. ht: 6-9 in *15-23 cm* dist: 6-9 in *15-23 cm* Aug-Nov, acid, full sun, semi-shade. Large deep-blue flowers, 1½ in (3.5 cm) long, with some green markings in the bold stripes on the corolla. Needs moisture without 'wetness', very free-flowering when conditions are right for it.

G. verna angulosa H. ht: 4-6 in *10-15 cm* dist: 6 in *15 cm* May-Jun, full sun, semi-shade. The grass-like foliage is often completely covered by the brightest blue flowers, ¾ in (2 cm) in diameter, which have a white eye. The calyx is prominently winged in this variety.

✳ **Geranium** (Crane's Bill) Nec/Pol H. ⬡
Geraniums are not the bright red-flowered bedding-plants (that look so much better in the bright sun of the south of France) familiar to us all. (They are in fact *Pelargonium*, a completely different and less versatile genus, at least in northern European climates.) The geraniums have everything to recommend them: ease of cultivation, long flowering seasons, lots of flowers, a wide range of colours, interesting leaves, not fussy over soil, and above all excellent bee plants. They are among the best of all herbaceous plants, thriving in north and south alike.

The flowers, carried singly or in terminal clusters, are five-petalled, the lobes rounded and notched, either flat or shallowly bowl-shaped, and 1-2 in (2.5-5 cm) across. The ten stamens are long and conspicuous. The fruit or seed pod is distinctly beaked, hence the common name, and this splits when ripe into arched or coiled sections.

The rounded leaves are palmately lobed, sometimes very deeply so.

G. cinereum H. ht: 6 in *15 cm* dist: 1 ft *30 cm* May-Sep, full sun. Deep pink, smallish bowl-shaped flowers with conspicuous dark red venation and a dark eye. The leaves are grey-green. The cultivar 'Ballerina' is white with crimson venation and eye. Good rock garden plants.

G. endressii H. ht: 18 in *45 cm* dist: 18 in *45 cm* Jun-Oct, semi-shade. Very pretty clusters of pale pink, red-veined smallish flowers set against grey-green leaves. There are several cultivars available, all of them with deeper pink flowers. A rhizomatous species, so take care when replanting or dividing.

G. himalayense syn. *grandiflorum* H. ht: 18 in *45 cm* dist: 18 in *45 cm* Jul-Aug, full sun. Deeply cut leaves and flat, almost round, large blue-purple flowers with a white eye. Rhizomatous. If you like the colour but not the size of this species, the cultivar 'Alpinum' grows no higher than 9 in (23 cm). There is also a variegated form.

G. macrorrhizum H. ht: 9 in *23 cm* dist: 18 in *45 cm* Jun-Jul, full sun, semi-shade. A real spreader, with small strongly aromatic leaves which may turn reddish in autumn. The small flowers are rosy-purple and are carried in clusters. Rhizomatous.

G. psilostemon ht: 3 ft *90 cm* dist: 2 ft *60 cm* Jun-Jul, full sun. Vivid medium-sized crimson-magenta flowers with a black eye. The leaves are deeply cut and may colour well in autumn.

G. renardii H. ht: 9 in *23 cm* dist: 9-12 in *23-30 cm* Jun-Jul, full sun. Worth growing for the sage-green, softly hairy, lobed and scalloped leaves alone. The leaf surfaces are so heavily net-veined that the whole leaf is rather like a quilt. The form in my own garden also has occasional splashes of gold in the leaves. The deeply notched, medium-sized, cup-shaped flowers are pale lilac, with darker venation. Short flowering season.

G. sanguineum 'Lancastriense' H. ht: 6 in *15 cm* dist: 12 in *30 cm* May-Nov, full sun. A wonderful little plant, almost too good to be true. The largish clear pink flowers just go on and on, almost covering the small downward-flexed leaves, which are rather like a clasped bird's foot. My own plants seed themselves freely and thrive even in compacted gravel paths.

Geum Nec/Pol H. ⬭

Showy herbaceous plants, superficially very similar to the herbaceous potentillas. The leaves grow from the base, and are usually much divided.

G. rivale (Water Avens) ht: 12 in *30 cm* dist: 9 in *23 cm* May-Sep, wet, semi-shade, shade. There is a world of difference between this dainty native plant, with its small, nodding yellow-buff flower heads, and the much more showy open-flowered garden types. *G. rivale* has hairy, reddish-purple sepals almost as long as the petals, and the flower, which is usually bee pollinated, is so packed with stamens that nectar extraction is a frustrating business for the bees. The seed heads are beautiful, rather like pink hairy spiders. It grows well enough on most soils, but thrives under wet conditions on

heavy soils, where little else that you want in your garden will grow. Not in the first rank of bee plants, but irresistible for anyone with wild garden aspirations!

G. x borisii ht: 12 in *30 cm* dist: 9-12 in *23-30 cm* May-Aug, full sun. The orange-scarlet flowers contrast beautifully with the bright green foliage.

G. chiloense ht: 2 ft *60 cm* dist: 18 in *45 cm* May-Sep, full sun. The bright orange flowers are carried in clusters on slender stems. Most of the geums grown in gardens are cultivars of *chiloense*, namely 'Mrs Bradshaw' (bright scarlet), 'Lady Stratheden' (golden yellow). Both these cultivars are, however, semi-double and therefore rather difficult for bees to work.

The ½ in (1.3 cm) diameter flowers of both *x borisii* and all the *chiloense* cultivars have rather crinkly petals.

Hamamelis (Witch Hazel) Pol. Shr. ⬭

ht: 10 ft *3 m* dist: 8-10 ft *2.5-3 m*
Dec-Mar, acid, full sun, semi-shade.
If you like the exotic, the fragrant yellow flowers of the rather gaunt Asian and eastern North American witch hazels will excite your interest. The four or more crinkly and strap-shaped petals push through the clusters of plump pale-brown flower buds on the leafless branches in very early spring. Each of the ¼ in (6 mm) chalice-like calyces has four short dull-red pointed sepals which give an attractive and contrasting dark eye to the flowers. The very open nature of the flowers ensures that the pollen is freely available, once these curious sheath-like sepals have released the anthers. The leaves are very similar to the hazel (see *Corylus*), but are more heavily veined and usually turn butter-gold in autumn.

Not very fast-growing plants, but they will eventually become too large for most gardens, although this rarely seems to stop the enthusiasts from cramming them in, and you can of course cut back any excessive growth from December to March and use it for flower arrangements, for which it is superb.

Plant groups of snowdrops and blue and

Hamamelis mollis 'Pallida', a valuable early source of pollen.

yellow crocus beneath the shrub to provide a cheerful sight for both man and bee in the late winter.

H. x intermedia 'Jelena' Dense clusters of large — well over 1 in (2.5 cm) — coppery-red flowers. Quite stunning. Red-orange and scarlet autumn leaf coloration.

H. mollis 'Pallida' Pale yellow flowers very freely carried. Autumn leaf colour yellow. Usually quite freely available and deservedly so, for this is a first-class plant.

* **Hebe** Nec. Shr.
salt tol, full sun
It is hardly surprising that the hebes were for many years grouped botanically with the veronicas, of which they are the shrubby counterparts. Not all species, however, have the very long flower spikes of the veronicas, but those that do, such as the *speciosa* hybrids, are amongst the most handsome of easily grown evergreen shrubs; unfortunately they also appear to be the least hardy. To make certain you are buying species likely to survive in your area, visit a local botanic garden or large park

and take note of which species are grown there.

Given reasonable conditions, hebes grow quickly and flower profusely. The small tubular flowers have four petals, one 'above' and three clustered below. There is no difficulty with nectar extraction, and some cultivars, such as 'Carl Teschner', will be alive with bees on a sunny day.

The leaves, which may be narrow and up to 4 in (10 cm) long, or, at the other extreme, compressed and scale-like, are carried in opposite pairs. If you must grow species which are not reliably hardy, then try and choose a sheltered spot. All the plants listed below are reasonably hardy and will survive in most cool temperate climates, such as the British Isles.

H. x andersonii 'Midsummer Beauty' ht: 4-5 ft *1.25-1.5 m* dist: 4-5 ft *1.25-1.5 m* Jun-Oct. A marvellous long-flowering cultivar with lavender-blue flowers and long narrow leaves.

H. armstrongii ht: 3 ft *1 m* dist: 3 ft *1 m* Jul-Aug. Cupressus-like shoots of olive green, yellow at the tips, with clusters of tiny white flowers. Rather stiff in habit.

84

H. x 'Autumn Glory' ht: 3 ft *90 cm* dist: 2 ft *60 cm* Aug-Nov. The blue-violet flowers are carried in short clusters above the dark oval leaves.

H. brachysiphon ht: 4 ft *1.25 m* dist: 3 ft *1 m* May-Jun. Dense clusters of pink-tipped buds, opening to white, crowd the branches in spring, beautifully complementing the small grey stalkless leaves.

The cultivar 'White Gem' is rather less vigorous.

H. x 'Carl Teschner' ht: 9 in *23 cm* dist: 2 ft *60 cm* Jun-Aug. Short clusters of lavender-blue flowers with a white throat. The wiry stems are a dull burgundy red and the leaves small and narrowly elliptic. A fine ground-cover plant.

H. x 'Great Orme' ht: 3 ft *1 m* dist: 3 ft *1 m* Aug-Oct. Leaves lance-shaped, up to 3 in (7.5 cm) long. The flowers are bright pink in long tapering clusters. A most elegant plant and hardier than most of the other *speciosa* hybrids — well worth trying.

Hebe 'Blue Gem'. The shrubby veronicas are very attractive to bees.

'Marjorie' ht: 3 ft *1 m* dist: 3 ft *1 m* Jul-Sep. A very hardy cultivar with blue-mauve flowers that fade to white, carried in clusters 3 in (7.5 cm) long.

H. pinguifolia 'Pagei' ht: 9 in *23 cm* dist: 18 in *45 cm* May-Jun. Due in part to its undoubted hardiness, this is probably the most commonly seen cultivar in cultivation. The elliptic grey leaves are often margined dull red, especially in winter. In May the short clusters of white flowers with their distinct reddish-brown anthers cover the whole plant, and are a splendid sight. I grow it close to blue winter-flowering pansies, purple *Aubrieta* and blue *Lithodora*, with a few winter aconites scattered around.

Hedera (Ivy) Nec/Pol Shr. ht: 3-4 ft *1-1.25 m* dist: 2-3 ft *60-90 cm* Sep-Dec, full sun, semi-shade

The common ivy, *Hedera helix*, is a familiar sight as it climbs up and sometimes over buildings and trees in town and country alike. The climbing shoots (which will trail equally well if there is nothing for them to cling to) are in fact the juvenile growth phase, and will bear 'typical' leathery ivy leaves with five pointed lobes, the two basal ones with a deep cordate base. Ivy is not a parasite and does not harm trees it climbs up. It is not necessary, therefore, to follow the practice of killing ivy to protect the tree, particularly as a large ivy provides a lot of food and shelter for birds as well as forage for bees. As the plant ages, and typically when it reaches the top of a building or tree, the whole growth pattern changes. Much thicker shoots without any tendency to climb are produced, and it is these shoots, and only these, that produce flowers and fruit once they reach sunlight. The leaves on these shoots have little or no lobing and are broadly oval in shape. This second growth phase is known as arborescent (or adult).

The juvenile phase is then of no interest to us at all as a bee plant. The arborescent phase may not, however, be reached for 15-20 years, and not many of us are prepared to be this patient! Interestingly, cuttings taken from arborescent shoots will, once rooted (and this can be a very slow process indeed), retain this characteristic, allowing the gardener to have 1-2 ft (30-60 cm) ivy bushes without any trailing shoots. Not many people apart from a few ivy fanatics, and I count myself one of these, would bother to go to this much trouble, but there are one or two very nice named cultivars that might be worth a try if you are looking for a very late source of a really concentrated nectar.

Flowering in late September and October, ivy provides the last nectar and pollen forage for the honey bee. Numerous large pinkish-brown loads of pollen are collected at the same time as nectar. In some parts of Britain beekeepers rely on ivy to provide most of their colonies' winter stores. The honey is high in the sugar glucose, and therefore crystallizes very quickly, but usually this does not cause any problems. Some idea of the concentration of the nectar can be gauged by the attraction it has for all types of flies, wasps and other insects, as well as bees. Ivy is, however, such a common plant, in all parts of Britain at least, that it really is not worth planting.

The individual flowers are around ¼ in (6 mm) in diameter, five-pointed and greenish, with a yellow central disc from which nectar is secreted. Each flower is on a long stalk, and there may be thirty or more flowers in each head. The flower stem may bear many secondary flower heads. The fruits are black, up to ⅓ in (8 mm) in diameter.

Remember that you are very unlikely to be able to buy arborescent forms of any of the species or cultivars listed below, but they are all good garden plants in their own right, and your patience will eventually be rewarded when they finally — after perhaps 15 years — start to produce arborescent flowering shoots.

H. colchica Very large leaves and freer-flowering than the variegated type.

'Dentata Variegata' A really nice cultivar with variable yellow variegation around the outside of the leaves. It is absolutely hardy.

H. canariensis 'Gloire de Marengo' syn. 'Ghost Tree', 'Variegata', *algeriensis* 'Gloire de Marengo'. Large handsome grey-green leaves with variable

creamy variegation around the outside of the leaves. Die-back of shoots may be a problem in severe winters.

Helianthemum (Rock Rose) Nec/Pol Shr.

ht: 9 in *23 cm* dist: 9-12 in *23-30 cm*
May-Jul, dry, salt tol, full sun
Descriptions and recommendations for *Halimum* and x *Halimocistus*, which are very similar to *Helianthemum*, are also given below.

As the name implies, these dwarf plants positively thrive in full sun, and indeed without it the masses of brilliant five-petalled flowers, in size and form rather like those of *Potentilla*, stay slightly closed on the ends of the thin wiry stems. The grey-green leaves contrast well with the brightly coloured flowers. Nectar is not produced in any great quantity unless the weather is very hot, but the large amounts of pollen carried over a very long season help to compensate for this.

None of the rock roses is particularly hardy, but they will withstand quite severe frosts if the soil is dry, so they do very well on hot dry banks, in or on walls and on light sandy soils. I have several plants in a really dry soil growing through gravel on a driveway, and they obviously enjoy this situation, for they never stop flowering from May to July. Cuttings root easily if taken in August. Several seed firms now offer seed, usually of mixed colours of yellow, orange, pink and scarlet; this should be sown in April to flower the following year (x *Halimocistus* is a hybrid and cannot be raised from seed, so cuttings have to be taken).

H. nummularium 'Ben Nevis' Deep yellow with a deeper eye. Foliage green.

'Fire Dragon' Orange-red flowers.

'The Bride' Creamy-white flowers with a yellow eye.

'Wisley Pink' Clear pink flowers with a shaded orange eye.

There are many other cultivars and an increasing number of seed-raised plants; take care when selecting plants, especially on a dull day when the flowers are not open, that you do not purchase any with double flowers.

Halimum ⬡ ht: 3 ft *90 cm* dist: 2-3 ft *60-90 cm* Rather larger in all its parts than *Helianthemum* but similar in other respects. All the species have yellow or white flowers.

x Halimocistus *Halimum x Cistus* 🌿 ht: 2 ft *60 cm* dist: 2 ft *60 cm* Blends the characteristics of both genera (see *Cistus*) and has slightly wider leaves. The species *wintonensis* is particularly attractive, with its large white satin-like flowers, with dark crimson-maroon markings 'feathering' down to the yellow-stained petal bases.

Helleborus (Hellebore or Bear's Foot) Nec/Pol H. 🌿 ⬡
full sun, semi-shade

Most valuable evergreen perennials flowering in late winter and early spring, producing copious amounts of both nectar and pollen. The handsome toothed, leathery leaves are divided into between three and twelve leaflets. The flowers may be carried singly or in nodding clusters, and vary in shape from flat to cup-shaped. The five or six 'petals' (actually sepals) are blunt and overlap each other, whilst the true petals are adapted into boomerang-shaped nectaries ⅓ in (8 mm) long, surrounding the mass of anthers. The flower structure is very similar to that of the winter aconites. Always purchase container-grown plants, since hellebores do not like root disturbance.

H. atrorubens ht: 12 in *30 cm* dist: 12 in *30 cm* Feb-Mar. Deep red-purple 2 in (5 cm) flowers, greenish within, carried in clusters. Clump-forming.

H. lividus corsicus syn. *corsicus* (Corsican Helle-bore) ht: 2 ft *60 cm* dist: 2 ft *60 cm* Feb-Apr. My own plants were collected (as seed) in Corsica, so the various name changes that this superb plant has been subjected to do not appeal to me in the least.

The glossy three-lobed leaves are sharply toothed, and these gradually deteriorate as new ones are produced from the centre of the rootstock after flowering; it is best to cut back the old shoots in June after flowering, unless

you wish to leave one or two to produce seed, which they will do very readily. The cup-shaped flowers are pale apple-green and are present in bud form from January. A really tough hardy plant which, along with many of the other hellebores, has what the landscape designers like to term 'architectural qualities'.

H. foetidus ht: 2 ft *60 cm* dist: 2 ft *60 cm* Feb-Apr. Surely this must be one of Europe's finest native plants, with its much divided, narrow, dark green leaves, for it always looks good but never more so than when the clusters of pendulous pale green flowers with purple edge striations are produced. The bracts that sub-tend the flowers can also be very showy, with finger-like projections that make them look like small palm trees. Do not be put off growing this marvellous plant by its common name — Stinking Hellebore.

H. niger (Christmas Rose) ht: 1 ft *30 cm* dist: 1 ft *30 cm* Dec-Apr. The flowering period of this species is very variable, in spite of its common name. The flowers are usually white, but may be tinged with pink or green. With flowers kept under cloches, to preserve their whiteness, I have seen honey bees working them on Christmas Day in southwest England.

The stinking hellebore, an unattractive name for a majestic plant, Helleborus foetidus.

The Lenten rose, Helleborus orientalis.

The cultivar 'Potter's Wheel' has very large, 4-5 in (10-2.5 cm), pure white flowers, and is a sight to behold when in full flower, pushing up through the winter snow.

H. orientalis (Lenten Rose) ht: 2 ft *60 cm* dist: 2 ft *60 cm* Feb-Mar. The 3 in (7.5 cm) bowl-shaped flowers are rather similar to those of *niger*, but they come in a range of colours from white to pink through to dark purple, and some have glorious spotting in contrasting colours.

Hydrangea Nec/Pol Shr. ⅂
semi-shade

The hydrangeas are excellent and easily grown garden plants, producing large rounded flower heads towards late summer. Unfortunately, many of the most commonly grown *macrophylla* (syn. *hortensis*) cultivars produce a preponderance of the more showy but sterile, or semi-sterile, individual flowers, which are of course virtually useless for honey bees. The ratio of fertile to sterile flowers can vary considerably

with cultivar, so it is vital to do some research before making your choice. Any of the species listed below, or cultivars from the so-called Lacecap groups, can be bought unseen in the knowledge that they produce large numbers of fertile flowers.

The sterile four-sepalled 'flowers' are too well known to require a detailed description. Each tiny ¼ in (6 mm) flower is star-like, the individual petals forming boat-shaped nectar carriers, and the mass of individual flowers, with their pale lemon or blue-tipped anthers, in strong light are not unlike a bright massed galaxy. The leaves are generally large and handsome, frequently taking on bronzish tints before they fall.

Contrary to popular opinion hydrangeas do not need acid soils to do well, but if grown on shallow chalky soils the leaves will show pale yellow patches, and blue-flowered cultivars will turn pink. This can be counteracted by mulching with peat and regular treatment with bluing compounds, which are readily available from garden centres.

H. anomala petiolaris ❀ Jun-Jul. A vigorous and attractive climber with broad pale-green leaves which turn butter-yellow in autumn. Even young plants produce aerial roots on the pale brown stems, which quickly anchor themselves to just about any surface.

Easily enough controlled by regular pruning which, since it is capable of reaching 30 ft (10 m) or more, will usually be necessary. If you neglect your pruning, then be prepared to have to take a saw to the limbs, which can easily reach arm thickness! The flower heads are greenish white and up to 10 in (25 cm) across, with a fringe of sterile flowers.

H. paniculata 'Grandiflora' ◯ ht: 6 ft *2 m* dist: 5 ft *1.5 m* Aug-Oct. Dense lilac-like (both in size and shape) heads of creamy white flowers — fertile and infertile mixed together — which age to pink. The old flower heads should be cut well back after flowering, and they can be dried and used for winter decoration if required. I always want to leave them until spring so their frost-laden tracery can be enjoyed through the winter. Certainly one of the best of all autumn-flowering shrubs.

H. quercifolia ◯ ht: 5 ft *1.5 m* dist: 4 ft *1.25 m* Aug-Sep. As the name suggests, the leaves strongly resemble those of the oak. White flowers similar to the Lacecap types listed below. Excellent autumn leaf coloration.

H. villosa ◯ ht: 6 ft *2 m* dist: 5-6 ft *1.5-2 m* Aug-Oct. Leaves and stems densely hairy. Beautiful large lilac-blue sepals, which are also toothed. Perhaps needs more shade than other species, and this in turn gives some protection to the easily frost-damaged new growth in spring.

LACECAPS ◯ Jul-Sep

Rather flat heads of fertile flowers, fringed with sterile ones. All are excellent garden plants.

'Blue Wave' ht: 6 ft *2 m* dist: 5-6 ft *1.5-2 m* Outer sepals may vary from pink to blue, depending on soil type.

'Lanarth White' ht: 4 ft *1.25 m* dist: 4 ft *1.25 m* Outer sepals white, inner ones blue or pink.

'Tricolor' ht: 6 ft *2 m* dist: 5-6 ft *1.5-2 m* Leaves variegated with grey and pale yellow. Flowers white to pale pink.

* **Hypericum** Pol. Shr. 🌿
The shrubby golden-flowered St John's Worts are adaptable and easy plants to grow, as witnessed by the large number of species and cultivars that have naturalized themselves in Britain and other areas of Europe. However, in spite of this tendency in some to 'take over', they are firm favourites in my garden for the shrub border or rock garden. Depending on their size, the flowers, which may be carried over many months, can be up to 3 in (7.5 cm) across, and are packed with literally hundreds of the most delicate thin stamens, topped with bifid anthers positively dripping with pollen (see back cover). As the five rounded petals open, the anthers themselves fold back to reveal the stigmas arising from the typical onion-shaped base. Once flowering is finished this swollen base becomes an attractive fruit in some species, and the calyx may take on red-orange coloration. Some species also have good autumn leaf colour.

H. androsaemum 🌿 ⚘ ht: 2-3 ft *60-90 cm* dist: 18-24 in *45-60 cm* Jul-Sep, semi-shade, shade. The small pale yellow flowers are carried in terminal clusters of up to five flowers. When the petals fall the calyx becomes red-green, and in the autumn the large palish green leaves also take on the same colours, making a very pretty picture, especially when the red berry-like fruits, later turning to purple-black, have also formed.

H. calycinum (Rose of Sharon) 🌿 ht: 18 in *45 cm* dist: 18 in *45 cm* Jul-Sep, semi-shade, shade. Definitely an invasive species, with a strongly suckering habit. No empty neighbouring piece of ground or even path is safe from its wanderings. I can, personally, forgive it anything in return for its truly marvellous pale gold flowers (carried singly) which are a full 3 in (7.5 cm) across. The rounded petals are widely spaced and the centre is packed with hundreds of yellow stamens, each topped with a dull red anther. The leaves are large, and are dark green and rounded — a nice complement to the flowers.

The plants can become very untidy if left unpruned, and I remember that when I had to look after large areas of·Rose of Sharon it received its biennial haircut with a rotary mower set at about 3-4 in (7.5-10 cm)!

H. x indorum 'Elstead' 🌿 ⚘ ht: 3-4 ft *1-1.25 m* dist: 2-2½ ft *60-75 cm* Jul-Sep, semi-shade, shade. For the flowers alone, which are small and yellow, I would not bother with this hybrid, but they are followed by the most exquisite coral-pink fruits in autumn.

H. olympicum 🌿 ht: 6-9 in *15-23 cm* dist: 9-12 in *23-30cm* Jun-Aug, full sun. Forms a dense mound covered with large golden 2 in (5 cm) flowers and small blue-green leaves. Ideal for wall crevices or rock gardens. *H. olympicum citrinum* is a showy lemon-yellow form.

H. patulum 'Hidcote' ht: 4-6 ft *1.25-2 m* dist 3 ft *1 m* Jul-Oct, full sun, semi-shade. 'Golden Saucer' is a good name for the clusters of large satin-textured flowers with orange anthers, which are freely carried throughout the summer. The leaves are dark green above, pale beneath and semi-evergreen. Quite simply 'a winner'.

Iberis Nec/Pol
dry, full sun

The candytufts are very free-flowering and extremely easy to grow, even on the poorest and driest of soils. The flat flower heads, which are up to 2 in (5 cm) in diameter, contain many florets, the inner ones small, the outer progressively larger. Each floret has four petals, the outer two of which are considerably larger than the inner, thus providing an excellent work platform for the bees.

I. saxatilis H/Shr. ht: 6 in *15 cm* dist: 12 in *30 cm* May-Jun. The dark green prostrate mats of foliage are smothered with dazzling white 6 in (15 cm) flower spikes in spring. An excellent rock garden plant. Cut back the flower spikes as soon as flowering is finished.

I. sempervirens 'Snowflake' H/Shr. ht: 12 in *30 cm* dist: 9 in *23 cm* Jun. The pure white rounded flower heads are 2 in (5 cm) or so in diameter — somewhat larger than those of *saxatilis*. At 9-12 in (23-30 cm) in height it is, however, a shade tall for the rock garden.

I. umbellata 'Dwarf Fairy' A(h). ht: 12-15 in *30-40 cm* dist: 9 in *23 cm* May-Oct. Easily raised from seed sown in situ, giving a variety of really pretty 'candy' coloured flowers — magenta, pinks, lavender and white — over a very long season. Left to their own devices the flattened seed cases will sow next year's crop for you, but they may not grow exactly where you want them to.

Ilex (Holly) T/Shr.
May-Jun, salt tol, full sun, semi-shade

The hollies are native to most of Europe, North and South America and Asia, where they are common large shrubs or trees in the wild. Holly is known to most people; if not in the wild, then through Christmas wreaths, decorations and cards — it is part of the traditional Christmas scene, and long may it continue to be so.

The thick leathery leaves are like burnished leather, with stiff prominent prickles pointing in all directions from the leaf margins. The branches retain their green coloration for many years, and in variegated forms pink or dark red striations are an additional attraction.

The fragrant flowers are small and white and are carried in the leaf axils. They secrete nectar freely and are well worked by honey bees. Male and female flowers are carried on separate plants, and this explains why many hollies never have berries (as these are obviously males or, to confuse the issue further, females without the benefit of local males!). An inspection of the flowers will, however, reveal the true state of things. The females bear berries, but will have no pollen. If you want berries then you will have to plant male and female plants in your garden, unless there are male plants very locally (which there usually are). Some species and cultivars will berry without pollination — see below. There is really no benefit to the bees in your having female berrying plants, since they do not act as a source of pollen. The blood-red berries are however irresistible, especially when contrasted with the dark green leaves: a wonderful sight on a winter's day, if you can get there before the birds.

Hollies were commonly used as hedging plants in the past, but their slow growth has caused them to fall from favour. If you have the patience then a holly hedge is a splendid sight and acts as foil for the more brightly coloured plants that might be placed in front of it. It is, however, unlikely to flower if it is clipped annually.

Holly is unfortunately an unreliable source of nectar and pollen; the flowering season is short, at around 2-3 weeks, and erratic, and in some years virtually non-existent. This may be linked to very low carbohydrate levels in the plant in years following heavy berry crops, and these may take several years to re-build. This is the hypothesis that has been put forward for the same problem with beech seed crops, and it may well hold good for holly too. Remember that variegated cultivars will need sunnier positions than their green counterparts, and that those cultivars with marginal coloration are more stable and less liable to revert than those with green leaf edges and central leaf coloration.

I x. altaclarensis 'Golden King' Nec. ht: 12-15 ft

3.5-4.5 m dist: 10-12 ft *3-3.5 m* In spite of its name this cultivar is female and is probably the best and most stable golden variegated holly. Being virtually spineless and easy to handle, it is ideal for wreaths and general decorations. The berries are large, but are not freely produced.

I. aquifolium 'Amber' Nec. ht: 12-15 ft *3.5-4.5 m* dist: 10-12 ft *3-3.5 m* Dark green shiny leaves with yellow-orange berries carried in tight clusters.

'Handsworth New Silver' Nec. ht: 12-15 ft *3.5-4.5 m* dist: 10-12 ft *3-3.5 m* A purple stemmed cultivar, leaves dark green with a cream edge; scarlet berries freely produced.

'Golden Queen' Nec/Pol ht: 12-15 ft *3.5-4.5 m* dist: 10-12 ft *3-3.5 m* A striking cultivar with exceptionally spiny, irregular, golden-margined leaves, the inner areas of which are a mid-green with paler grey shading. The shoots are a dull burgundy with paler pink striations. This is a male cultivar that bears no berries, but it is still an outstanding plant, and useful for both nectar and pollen for the bees.

'J.C. Van Tol' Nec/Pol ht: 12-15 ft *3.5-4.5 m* dist: 10-12 ft *3-3.5 m* A very free-berrying cultivar with almost spineless dark green leaves. Berries scarlet.

'Pyramidalis' Nec/Pol ht: 12-15 ft *3.5-4.5 m* dist: 10-12 ft *3-3.5 m* An upright cultivar that, like 'J.C. Van Tol', will produce fruit even if it is planted on its own, which suggests that the flowers are either bi-sexual or the berries are produced without fertilization, in which case they will be seedless.

The leaves are virtually spineless, and the scarlet berries are usually freely produced.

'Silver Queen' Nec/Pol ht: 12-15 ft *3.5-4.5 m* dist: 10-12 ft *3-3.5 m* The leaves are dark green with a cream margin and very spiny. The young leaves are often pinkish cream. No berries.

I. cornuta 'Rotunda' Nec/Pol ht: 4 ft *1.25 m* dist: 2-3 ft *60-90 cm* Not common in the average garden centre, but worth hunting for if you want a dwarf plant with the most interesting leaf shape of any of the hollies. The leaves are almost rectangular with a narrowed 'waist', and look rather like an animal skin pinned out to

dry! The fruits are large and are produced only sparingly, without pollination.

I. crenata 'Golden Gem' Nec. ht: 3 ft *1 m* dist: 2 ft *60 cm* Even slower growing than the previous cultivar, and entirely without spines; leaves yellow, berries black.

* **Impatiens** Nec/Pol Ann.
full sun, shade
The development of dwarf 'Busy Lizzies' suitable for summer bedding schemes has spiced up the rather staid displays in many a garden or park. They are quite excellent plants and are available in a wide range of glowing colours. They thrive equally well in bright sunshine or the semi-shade into which most British summers deteriorate. The fleshy stems bear attractive toothed leaves.

One of the three sepals is modified into a curved spur 1½ in (3.5 cm) long, in which nectar is held — quite inaccessible, it might seem. In warm weather, however, the nectar wells to the very top of the spur, where it can be easily extracted by honey bees. There are five flat overlapping petals.

I. novette hybrids ht: 6 in *15 cm* dist: 9 in *23 cm* Jun-Sep. Available in single colours, orange, red, pink, rose, salmon, and, of course, mixed. Better weather resistance than other bedding types.

I. glandulifera (Himalayan Balsam, Policeman's Helmet) ht: 4-5 ft *1.25-1.5 m* dist: 18 in *45 cm* Jul-Sep. The flowers of this (and other species naturalized throughout Europe) are quite distinct from the cultivated types and are very freely worked by the honey bees. Appreciable amounts of honey are stored in areas where this plant is abundant. Superficially the flowers resemble those of the *Antirrhinum*, but the 1 in (2.5 cm) triangular flower tube is in fact a modified sepal which provides for easy bee access — the bee walks in and then probes for nectar in the downward-pointing green spur. They do this avidly, in spite of the small quantities held there, even on dull cool autumn days, when they emerge covered in white pollen from the mass of anthers in the 'roof' of the flower. The flowers are quite simply beautiful in form and colour, ranging from white to pink through to purple, with foxglove-like spots and markings both inside and outside the sepal tube. This species, like the others, will thrive equally well in boggy conditions or bone-dry sandy soil in shade. I have encouraged it into the wilder fringes of my own garden, and I watch its progress with great pleasure. After the first touch of frost the fleshy red-green translucent stems collapse, but the plants re-seed themselves freely enough.

* **Kniphofia** Nec/Pol H.
dry, full sun

Red-hot-pokers, as *Kniphofia* is commonly called, are certainly one of the most distinctive of all garden plants, forming great multiple clumps with masses of long narrow leaves. Above the leaves rise the stiffly erect 'pokers', packed tight with masses of individual flowers. The basal flowers always open first, and in many of the older cultivars are a paler colour than the upper ones, giving a two-tone effect, often red above and yellow beneath.

A casual look at the tubular flowers would suggest that the nectar source is inaccessible, but run your hand over the poker-shaped head and it will come away sticky with nectar. So much is in fact produced that it dribbles down the thick stems. This makes them very popular with bees of all sorts, and a number may be seen working the head at the same time.

I can never bring myself to follow the recommended practice of tying the leaves together to help protect the crown of the plant against winter frost and wetness, for the foliage is handsome even in winter, but I have to admit the loss of one or two plants as a consequence. As an alternative, pile some peat or sawdust around the crown to a depth of 2 in (5 cm) or so.

Choose your planting site carefully to avoid having to move the plants again for at least 4-5 years: the roots are thick and fleshy and do not respond well to being disturbed.

Kniphofia species are all first-rate 'architec-tural' plants in the herbaceous or shrub border, and help to relieve the monotony of the 'burial mound' syndrome which seems to afflict all too many gardens!

K. caulescens ht: 3 ft *1 m* dist: 3 ft *1 m* Sep-Oct. The broad, blue-green, keeled foliage, rather like *Yucca*, makes this an outstanding species. The dense flower heads are 'traditional' in colour, yellow at the base and red at the tips. Needs some protection in colder areas.

K. galpinii ht: 2½ ft *75 cm* dist: 2½ ft *75 cm* Sep-Oct. A neat version of its larger more robust fellows, with orange flowers shading to a pale-orange yellow at their tips. An excellent plant for the autumn garden.

K. northiae ht: 4 ft *1.25 m* dist: 4 ft *1.25 m* Aug-Sep. Grown principally for its bold grey-green foliage, which can be up to 6 in (15 cm) wide at the base, and 4 ft (1.25 m) long. Flowers red, ageing to yellow.

K. sparsa syn. *modesta* ht: 2 ft *60 cm* dist: 2 ft *60 cm* Jul-Aug. Neither name sounds terribly promis-ing, but this is a subtly pleasing species, with its pale pink flower buds opening to an ivory white.

K. uvaria Jun-Sep. The bulk of the plants offered for sale are derived from this species, which has narrow grey-green keeled leaves, toothed towards the tip. Most will flower for 2-3 months.

'Bee's Sunset' Flower heads uniformly gold.

'Burnt Orange' ht: 2½ ft *75 cm* dist: 2½ ft *75 cm* Flowers pale brown opening to orange.

'Maid of Orleans' ht: 3½ ft *105 cm* dist: 3½ ft *105 cm* White flowers.

'Royal Standard' ht: 3½ ft *105 cm* dist: 3½ ft *105 cm* The most commonly seen and popular cultivar, with handsome two-tone flower heads of red and yellow.

'Samuel's Sensation' ht: 6 ft *2 m* dist: 5 ft *1.5 m* The giant of the group, with brilliant red flowers.

Kniphofia uvaria, this unusual red-hot-poker is a striking 'architectural' plant, and well worth looking for.

*Lamium (Deadnettles) Nec/Pol H. 芈 semi-shade

The common name is hardly appealing, but it merely means that these are non-stinging types of nettle-like plants.

The leaves of all those mentioned below are coarsely toothed, pungent and are carried on rather lax square-section stems. The flowers are carried in a succession of erect leafy terminal whorls, and even before one has finished flowering the next is ready to take its place. There may be four or five separate flowering 'layers' produced on each stem in a season. The individual flowers may be up to 1 in (2.5 cm) long and are distinctly two-lipped, the lower broadly two-lobed and serrated. The upper lip, or hood, shelters the flower tube and prevents moisture entering and diluting the nectar.

The four stamens are attached low down on the back of the hood, and the tiny figure-of-eight anthers are usually of a colour that contrasts strongly with the flower: black for the white, and orange for the red wild deadnettles.

Nectar is secreted even on very cold autumn days well into November, or until the flowers are frost-damaged. But it may not always be available to honey bees if the flower tubes are long. It is not uncommon to see the base of the tube holed by bumble bees in order to get at the nectar, and this also makes access easier for the honey bee. Pollen is also collected, and the wild deadnettle (*L. purpureum*), flowering as early as February, is a useful source at a time when little else is available.

I have never seen the 'weed' types intentionally grown in a garden, but the flowers are beautiful nevertheless. Many beekeepers are interested in the conservation of bees in general, and the purple deadnettle, *L. purpureum*, and the white deadnettle, *L. album* are two major bumblebee plants. The latter is probably one of the most nectar-productive of all plants for the amount of space it occupies. So if you can afford a little wild area in your garden these are two plants to encourage.

L. maculatum 'Beacon Silver' ht: 6 in *15 cm* dist: 9 in *23 cm* May-Oct. A really striking ground-cover plant with silver, conspicuously net-veined foliage, intermittently spotted with purple. Only the very edges of the leaves are green. The prolific deep-pink flowers sit very prettily atop the grey leaves.

'Shell Pink' ht: 6 in *15 cm* dist: 1 ft *30 cm* May-Oct. The leaves have an irregular splash of grey down their centres, and the flowers are a clear shell-pink. There has to be a space for this and the previous cultivar in the smallest of gardens.

L. galeobdolon 'Variegatum' (Yellow Archangel) ht: 1 ft *30 cm* dist: 2-3 ft *60-90 cm* May-Jun. A really rampant ground-cover plant that sends out long runners which root at the nodes, smothering any less vigorous plants in its path. I have it planted next to 'Beacon Silver' and 'Shell Pink', and very regular disentangling sessions are required.

The leaves are large, up to 4 in (10 cm) long by 3 in (7.5 cm) wide, coarsely toothed and irregularly splotched with two broad silver bands. The conspicuous yellow flowers are carried on erect stems. The correct generic name for this plant is now *Lamiastrum*, but old habits die hard.

Laurus nobilis (Bay Laurel) Nec. Shr. 🌿
⚘
ht: 12 ft *3.5 m* dist: 8-10 ft *2.5-3 m*
May-Jun, full sun, semi-shade

This plant is, in Britain at least, rather more interesting to me as a distinct flavouring for casseroles than as a truly decorative garden plant. There is, however, a universal mania for growing them in pots or tubs, especially for the small town garden, and trimmed to a variety of unusual shapes. This has probably arisen as a result of too many trips to the Mediterranean countries, where these rather easily wind- and frost-damaged plants are commonly clipped into all manner of shapes, but usually on a much grander scale, as in the Boboli gardens in Florence. Although the upper parts are subject to frost damage, the roots (as long as they are planted in the ground and not kept in pots) are as tough as old boots, and new shoots are readily produced from them.

Left to its own devices, the bay laurel will form a large pyramidal tree, but for reasons already discussed this is unlikely to happen in Britain, apart from in the milder western areas.

The masses of inconspicuous yellow-green flowers produce nectar freely during mild weather. If you are interested in having berries (these are shiny, small and black), you must obtain a female plant. The species *angustifolia* has narrower pale green leaves with wavy edges, and is said to be hardier, whilst *a.* 'Aurea' has leaves of golden yellow.

For the evergreen common laurels, see *Prunus*.

Lavandula (Lavender) Nec/Pol Shr. 🌿

Jul-Aug, dry, salt tol, full sun

I was familiar with the fragrance of lavender through soaps, oils, scents and lavender bags long before I knew what the plant even looked like, and it is nice to see that in spite of more exotic fragrances now available, lavender products are still firm favourites.

On a hot sunny summer day the normal heady fragrance becomes more obvious and, in the dry heat of a Spanish sierra, even pervasive, but always pleasant.

The short dark-mauve flowers are carried in several closely tiered heads on long thin stalks, and these are invariably covered with bees during mid summer. You will know what a good bee plant lavender is when other books warn you (as they do) not to stick your nose into the flowers for fear of being stung. The grey-green lance-like leaves are also strongly aromatic.

Lavenders look well when mixed with other plants with contrasting leaf shapes, such as *Senecio* 'Sunshine' and any of the *Potentilla* species, both of which have yellow flowers that complement the blue of the lavender very well. Dwarf forms can be used in rock gardens or dry stone walls. All lavenders tend to become leggy, so trim back the old flower spikes and some of the foliage straight after flowering, taking care not to cut back the stems bare of any green leaves.

Lavenders are common plants in southern Europe, and it is unlikely that you could find a

Lavandula stoechas, the 'French Lavender Rabbit'.

honey from these areas that did not have some lavender in its makeup. It is a major honey plant where it is grown on a field scale.

L. angustifolia syn. *officinalis* and *spica* ht: 2 ft *60 cm* dist: 18 in *45 cm* Sold under a variety of names, but commonly known as 'Old English Lavender'. The most highly scented variety, with lavender-blue flowers.

'Hidcote' syn. 'Nana Atropurpurea' ht: 1 ft *30 cm* dist: 9-12 in *23-30 cm* Silvery leaves, purple flowers. A good dwarf variety.

L. stoechas ht: 2 ft *60 cm* dist: 18 in *45 cm* The French lavender is not entirely hardy, but it is easily raised from collected seed and will produce the odd flower even in its first season. This sounds like a lot of trouble, but it is such a different plant and is so popular with the bees that I think the effort is worthwhile. The individual flowers, which are deep purple, are packed closely together and topped by three or four paler purple bracts, sticking up just like rabbit's ears. The sub-species *pedunculata* (if you can find it) is even more showy, with paler bracts up to 2 in (5 cm) long.

* **Lavatera** Nec/Pol ⚜
full sun

The hardy annuals and herbaceous perennials of this genus are perhaps more seen in gardens than the shrubs. All, however, have fine glistening satin-like flowers carried in leafy terminal clusters. The stamens, of which there are masses, fan out from a trunk-like base which is fused to the petals. The whole structure looks very like a small frost-laden tree. The cluster of spreading stigmas protruding through the centre of the 'tree' completes the picture. There is, of course, white pollen in abundance, so much so that bees working the flowers come away completely covered in it.

L. arborea Shr. ht: 4-6 ft *1.25-2 m* dist: 2 ft *60 cm* Aug-Sep. The tree mallow is often grown as a biennial but will survive in warmer districts and reach 10 ft (3 m) or so. The flowers are 3 in (7.5 cm) in diameter, and pale rose-purple. The leaves are softly hairy and may have 5-9 lobes.

L. olbia 'Rosea' H. ht: 3-4 ft *1-1.25 m* dist: 12-18 in *30-45 cm* Aug-Sep. Slightly larger reddish-purple flowers, distinctly bi-lobed, petals not quite overlapping as they do in other species. Leaves woolly and three-lobed.

L. trimestris A(h). ht: 12 in *30 cm* dist: 9 in *23 cm* Jul-Oct. The hardy annual mallows have received a lot of attention from the plant breeders over the last few years, and few plants can have repaid this attention so well, the shallow trumpet-shaped flowers being most attractive to the eye. Most grow to about 2 ft (60 cm).

'Loveliness' Flowers deep rose.

'Mont Blanc' Flowers glistening white.

'Silver Cup' Flowers glowing pink.

Ligustrum (Privet) Nec/Pol Shr.
full sun, semi-shade

A much derided shrub (or small tree), usually deciduous but evergreen in mild areas. Known to all as a hedging plant and regarded almost universally as the very epitome of all that is worst in a garden plant. There are, however, some very attractive species and cultivars

available, especially when they are grown as free-standing shrubs, unpruned, when masses of the small white tubular flowers are carried in erect pyramidal inflorescence, which could be said to have a smell rather than a scent. Blackish-purple fruits may follow in some instances, but these are soon taken by birds.

To me the wheel has turned full circle and the Leyland Cypress, golden or green, which has steadily replaced the privet in so many situations, is far more boring than the privet, of which the species *vulgare* is a plant native to much of Europe and very attractive to bees.

Honey from privet is said to have an objectionable smell and to be strongly flavoured, but it is unlikely that enough of it is ever made (the privet in flower being a quite uncommon sight) for this to be anything to worry about.

L. ovalifolium 'Aureum' ⚜ ht: 9 ft *2.75 m* dist: 6 ft *2 m* Aug-Sep. Not as floriferous as the species, but its golden-edged leaves make it such a welcome sight in the dull winter months that perhaps this slight failing can be forgiven, especially since it will be very useful in flower arrangements. In full sun many of the leaves will be almost entirely golden, with only narrow irregular green markings down the main vein.

L. sinense ⬭ ht: 10-12 ft *3-3.5 m* dist: 8 ft *2.5 m* Aug-Sep. This handsome species has long dense sprays of white flowers and is enthusiastically worked by bees.

* Limnanthes douglasii Nec/Pol A(h).
〒
ht: 6 in *15 cm* dist: 9 in *23 cm*
May-Sep, full sun

If you would like a showy white and yellow summer carpet, then this is the plant for you. The bees certainly like it. It has been called 'Bee Flower' because honey bees are so attracted to it that it is rarely seen (unless the weather is cold and wet) without its attendant bees busily collecting both nectar and loads of yellow pollen.

The masses of slightly cupped, sweetly scented flowers have five shallowly notched petals and are white, 1 in (2.5 cm) across, with a very prominent yellow eye. Its common name,

Sometimes called meadow foam, Limnanthes douglasii is another prolific plant loved by bees.

Poached or Fried Egg Plant, is an apt one. The much divided leaves are yellowish green, and the rather weak stems give the whole plant a straggling habit. Its natural habitat is damp marshy areas, but it will grow without too much trouble even in dry soil. Once you have grown *Limnanthes* you will never be without it — it seeds down readily and appears year after year, gradually spreading in area unless checked.

Linaria (Toadflax) Nec/Pol
Jun-Oct, full sun
The flower structure, if not the name, will be familiar to all, since it is very similar to that of *Antirrhinum* with its 'Snapdragon' closed lips. The lower lip of the flower may be a similar or contrasting colour. But, unlike *Antirrhinum*, the very pretty flowers are small enough for the honey bee's weight to open them, so access can be gained to the nectar and pollen. This is held in a ½ in (1.3 cm) narrow tapering 'horn', and during warm weather it will build up to a sufficient height for some of the excess to be drawn off. (Apropos of *Antirrhinum*, since they will not be mentioned again, there are now open-flowered types that allow honey bees access for nectar and pollen.)

L. alpina (Alpine Toadflax) A(h) ⚎ ht: 3 in 7.5 cm dist: 9 in 23 cm Purple-blue flowers with an orange lip and fleshy grey-green foliage. It will grow in the poorest of soils as long as it has sun. Ideal for the rock garden, where it will usually seed itself quite happily.

L. maroccana 'Excelsior' A(h). ht: 12 in 30 cm dist: 9 in 23 cm Wide range of colours in shades of yellow, pink, blue, red and purple.

'Fairy Bouquet' A(h). ht: 9 in 23 cm dist: 6-9 in 15-23 cm Wide colour range as above. Both these cultivars should be sown in situ in March or April in association with other annuals, or at the front of herbaceous or shrub borders.

L. purpurea H. ht: 3 ft 90 cm dist: 2 ft 60 cm Flowers bluish-purple with a white bearded mouth.

L. vulgaris (Common Toadflax) H. ◯ ht: 1-2 ft *30-60 cm* dist: 9 in *23 cm* The flowers are a sulphury yellow with an orange lip and striated spur. In common with many other hedgerow plants, the widely distributed common toad-flax, found throughout Europe (except in Portugal), has made something of a comeback in recent years, due entirely to the reduced frequency of verge mowing.

* **Lithodora** (syn. **Lithospermum**) *diffusum* 'Heavenly Blue' Nec. Shr. 🌿 ≢
ht: 2 ft *60 cm* dist: 2-4 ft *60-120 cm*
Apr-Jul, acid, dry, full sun, semi-shade
Perhaps there are not too many people lucky or foolish enough to say they have never yearned for soil or climate very different from the one they have. I have always counted myself as one of those lucky (or foolish) persons, but I should be very sad indeed if I now moved back to an area with alkaline soil and could not success-fully grow this jewel of a plant. To see sheets of it in the wild, cascading over rocks like a blue waterfall, is a sight once seen never forgotten. It will also grow perfectly well on the flat, and it is a rampant grower needing to be restrained annually, although it rarely exceeds 6-9 in (15-23 cm) in height.

The lance-shaped to oval leaves are dark green above, paler beneath, up to 1 in (2.5 cm) long and covered with short stiff hairs. The leaf margins are rolled downwards. The small flowers are carried in terminal clusters, and have five broadly rounded petals which narrow suddenly to a tube, ⅓ in (8 mm) or so in length. The petals are gentian blue, and the tube tends more towards a purplish blue. The tube might be thought rather long for bees, but it does fill with nectar and is a real favourite with them.

L. oleifolium ht: 12 in *30 cm* dist: 12-18 in *30-45 cm* Jun-Sep. Leaves larger and broader than the previous species, silkily hairy beneath. The more open, bell-shaped pale blue flowers allow easy access for bees. More tender than 'Heavenly Blue'.

Lobelia Nec. Ann. ◯
ht: 6 in *15 cm* dist: 9 in *23 cm*
May-Oct, full sun
These are best known as dwarf, blue, summer-flowering bedding plants (see *erinus* below), often used in conjunction with *Lobularia* — one white one, one blue one, one white one, etc., etc. There are, however, some striking erect herbaceous species (and a few evergreen shrubs), but unfortunately most of these have flower tubes too long for the honey bee.

L. erinus ht: 6 in *15 cm* dist: 6-9 in *15-23 cm* May-Oct. The pale-blue flowers are distinctly two-lipped: two narrow lobes above and three rather broad ones below (rather like the Marsh Orchid), with a white or yellowish eye. The flowers stud the domed plants right through to the first frosts. A large number of cultivars are available, all virtually the same except for the flower colour.

'Blue Pearl' Deep blue flowers with a small white eye.

'Crystal Palace' Deep blue flowers, with the added attraction of purplish-bronze foliage.

'Rosamund' Showy carmine flowers with white eye.

'Blue Cascade', 'Sapphire' and 'Red Cascade' are trailing cultivars, but are only really suitable for use in window boxes or hanging baskets, or for cascading over dry stone walls or rocks.

Lobularia maritima syn. **Alyssum maritima** (Sweet Alyssum) Nec/Pol A(h). ◯
ht: 6 in *15 cm* dist: 6 in *15 cm*
May-Oct, dry, salt tol, full sun
The 'other half' of the blue and white edging that forms such a well known part of so many summer bedding schemes. Now, in addition to white there is a wide range of flower colours available, all producing masses of fragrant, typically small cruciferous flowers in rounded heads which provide large quantities of both nectar and pollen.

It seems unlikely that most people will want to use the new name of this genus, particularly when seed firms market such cultivars as 'Wonderland' —*Alyssum* 'Wonderland' has more public appeal as a name than *Lobularia* 'Wonderland'! For all that, it is a superb cultivar with its rosy-red flowers. Pink, lilac and purple-flowered cultivars are also available.

The seed may be sown in March or April where it is to flower, and the plants thrive on the poorest and driest of soils.

Lonicera (Honeysuckle) Nec/Pol Shr.
full sun, semi-shade

The climbing Loniceras, with their marvellously fragrant long tubular flowers, so well adapted for the long tongues of moths and butterflies but so inaccessible to bees, immediately spring to mind whenever the honeysuckles are mentioned. This genus is, however, far more variable than most people imagine, and it also boasts some excellent deciduous and evergreen non-climbing shrubs. The flowers vary enormously in size, depending on species, and are carried in pairs in the shrubby species, whilst the climbers have terminal or axillary clusters.

CLIMBERS

L. japonica ht: 15 ft *4.5 m* Jun-Oct. The only climbing honeysuckle with flower tubes short enough for bees to extract nectar. A vigorous evergreen or semi-evergreen species with short 1 in (2.5 cm) flowers, white at first, changing to yellow as they age. Not particularly showy but a fast grower and the fragrance is delicious. The cultivar 'Aureoreticulata', with yellow leaf venation, is a beautiful plant, but unfortunately it rarely bears any flowers.

SHRUBS

L. fragrantissima ht: 6 ft *2 m* dist: 6 ft *2 m* Feb-Apr. Semi-evergreen with small, ½ in (1.3 cm) fragrant creamy flowers carried on the semi-naked branches in late winter and spring. The species *standishii* is similar, whilst *x purpusii* (the result of a union between *fragrantissima* and *standishii*) is slightly less vigorous but otherwise very similar.

L. involucrata syn. *ledebourii* ht: 8 ft *2.5 m* dist: 8 ft *2.5 m* Jun-Jul. A robust leafy shrub,

definitely not everyone's cup of tea, but the yellow flowers are carried in large numbers and upon close inspection are very attractive, surrounded as they are by two conspicuous rather waxy red bracts. These persist and contrast nicely with the small black fruits.

L. syringantha ht: 5 ft *1.5 m* dist: 5 ft *1.5 m* May-Jun. A rather slow-growing, stiff yet arching shrub with ½ in (1.3 cm) fragrant tubular flowers of a soft lilac.

L. tatarica ht: 9 ft *2.75 m* dist: 9 ft *2.75 m* May-Jun. Produces masses of pink flowers which are followed by red berries.

The evergreen honeysuckles such as *nitida* and *pileata* tend to be grown more as trimmed hedges than as specimens in their own right. They do not flower at all freely in cooler climates and, of course, clipping them ensures they have very little chance of ever doing so.

Lysimachia (Loosestrife) Nec/Pol H.
The three species described in the text are so different from each other that one could be forgiven for thinking they were from separate genera.

L. clethroides ht: 3 ft *90 cm* dist: 2 ft *60 cm* Aug-Oct, full sun, semi-shade. The long 'kinked' white flower heads look rather like those of the more graceful of the hebes, and give this plant its common name 'Gooseneck Loosestrife'. A splendid rhizomatous clump-forming plant with good autumn tints that is certainly not planted as widely as it deserves to be.

L. nummularia (Creeping Jenny) ht: 3 in *7.5 cm* dist: 18 in *45 cm* Jul-Aug, full sun, semi-shade. A real spreader, with branched creeping stems clothed with opposite rounded leaves. The erect, bright yellow, slightly cupped flowers, ¾ in (2 cm) across, are freely produced, one from each leaf axil. Planted next to more vigorous plants its invasive nature will be curbed. The golden-leaved form 'Aurea' is very attractive, but flowers less freely.

L. punctata ht: 3 ft *90 cm* dist: 2 ft *60 cm* Jul-Aug, full sun, shade. A rather stiff unbranched plant with leaves opposite or in whorls, lance-shaped with hairy margins. Numerous yellow flowers, ¾ in (2 cm) in diameter, carried in the leaf axils. Each whorl flowers at the same time, producing a mass of 3 ft (90 cm) yellow spikes. The eye is slightly darker than the ground-colour of the flower.

This is the most invasive of the three species, requiring a firm hand at the end of each growing season. It is often quite well established in the wild, in ditches and woodland throughout Europe.

Lythrum (Purple Loosestrife) Nec/Pol H.

Jun-Oct, wet, full sun, semi-shade

The purple loosestrife is now rarely seen in cultivation. It is, however, a splendid sight growing wild in great clumps by the riverside, the foot-long (30 cm) rose-purple flower spikes held stiffly erect, and how well it looks with that other native of damp places, the creamy meadowsweet.

Although it prefers damp conditions, it will do well enough in any good soil that is reasonably moisture-retentive. The bright six-petalled purple or pink propeller-like flowers are about 1 in (2.5 cm) in diameter, and have lemon-green stamens. These are of three different lengths, and produce three different sizes of pollen grains — the shorter the stamen the smaller the grain — a most unusual feature. An excellent bee plant for nectar and pollen for summer and autumn.

L. salicaria 'Firecandle' ht: 2-3 ft *60-90 cm* dist: 18 in *45 cm* Flowers intense rose-red.

'Robert' ht: 18-24 in *45-60 cm* dist: 18 in *45 cm* Flowers bright pink.

L. virgatum 'Rose Queen' ht: 18 in *45 cm* dist: 12 in *30 cm* Bright rose-red, but the flower spikes are less robust than the other species.

Magnolia Pol. Shr.

acid, full sun, semi-shade

I never really understood why people raved about Magnolias until I had seen the beautiful lily-shaped flowers of *M. denudata* (Lily Tree), standing erect in rows on naked horizontal branches, for all the world like pure white pine cones. The plant in question was some 15 ft (4.5 m) high, set in a sheltered semi-woodland setting, and the spring sky was blue. Being in South Devon the waxy flowers of this and other magnolias were not often damaged by frosts, as they are so commonly in colder climes. Most keen gardeners are prepared to risk frost damage for the one year in three to five when no flower damage occurs. Keen beekeepers, however, may not be so tolerant of a plant that, in Britain at least, appears to yield pollen only.

The majority of magnolias are far too large for the average garden, and only relatively small species are mentioned here.

M. liliiflora ht: 9 ft *2.75 m* dist: 7-8 ft *2.25-2.5 m* Apr-Jun. Flowers erect, with a purple flush on the outside of the petals, eventually opening to reveal a creamy-white interior.

'Nigra' ht: 7-8 ft *2.25-2.5 m* dist: 6 ft *2 m* Apr-Jun. Darker purple exterior to the petals, white inside with purple staining. Rather more compact than the species.

M. x soulangeana ht: 12 ft *3.5 m* dist: 10-12 ft *3-3.5 m* Apr-May. Many cultivars of this vigorous species, with wide spreading branches, are seen in cultivation. The large flowers are tulip-shaped, and white with purplish staining at their bases. It is more tolerant of lime than many species, and seen in combination with yews (as in churchyards) it is a marvellous sight when in full flower.

M. stellata (Star Magnolia) ht: 5-7 ft *1.5-2.25 m* dist: 6 ft *2 m* Mar-Apr. A fabulous plant, slow growing like all magnolias, but well worth the wait to see a bush covered with the starry flowers, each composed of sixteen narrow petals. The fragrant flowers are in fact much more resistant to frost and wind damage than any of the other cultivars or species with which I am familiar. The grey hairy winter buds are an attractive feature.

Pink-flowered cultivars 'Rosea' and 'Rubra' may also be available in good garden centres.

All magnolias benefit from being sheltered from cold winds in spring.

Fragrant and floriferous, Mahonia x media 'Charity' is also a useful 'conservation' plant, providing nectar and pollen for the bees, and berries for the birds.

Mahonia Nec/Pol Shr.
full sun, semi-shade

No garden should be without at least one of these handsome evergreens, with their glossy, dark-green, pinnately-divided leaves, which can be up to 2 ft (60 cm) long and often take on beautiful red tints during the winter months. The new growth also takes on pinky-red coloration in spring. Individual leaflets, which are pale beneath, are holly-like in shape, size and prickliness.

The flowers are, however, the crowning glory; deep primrose in colour, ⅓ in (8 mm) in diameter, produced in long or short terminal or axillary clusters and most deliciously scented —reminiscent of lily-of-the-valley. These are followed in all species by clusters of small, bloomy, blue-black fruits, which are usually quickly taken by birds, with the consequence that the fully developed fruits are rarely seen.

The six stamens are inserted into shallow depressions at the base of each petal and it is here that the nectar collects, and exceedingly sweet it is too. The flowers are extremely attractive to honey bees, and the flowering time makes it a very useful plant to fill in periods when other forage flowers are scarce, especially in a suburban district where oilseed rape is absent.

M. aquifolium (Oregon Grape) ht: 4-5 ft *1.25-1.5 m* dist: 3-7 ft *1-2.25 m* Mar-May. By far the most common species seen in cultivation, but fast being replaced by more exotic cultivars.

The rich yellow flower spikes are short and are carried both terminally and in the leaf axils. The leaves are in scale with the flowers, and can be very highly coloured — including the leaf stalks and veins in winter.

A very easily grown plant that will tolerate quite dense shade and which can be hacked back to ground level if it becomes overwhelming or too anti-social!

The cultivar 'Atropurpurea' has even darker red-purple leaves in winter.

M. x media 'Charity' ht: 6 ft *2 m* dist: 5-6 ft *1.5-2 m* Dec-Mar. A really bold plant, the darling of the landscape fraternity (and quite rightly so), with its 2 ft (60 cm) rather pointed leaves and long erect terminal flower spikes carried over a much longer period than any other cultivar.

M. japonica ht: 6 ft *2 m* dist: 5-6 ft *1.5-2 m* Jan-Mar. Like *x media* 'Charity', the leaves are large and handsome but the rather lax pale-primrose flower spikes are far more elegant. A superb plant.

There are many other species and cultivars, all of which are suitable for garden use since none of them bears double flowers.

Mahonias look well mixed with deciduous plants to give contrast or as specimens amongst lower growing ground-cover plants. If they do become too large then they may be cut back very hard, and this will encourage new shoots to be produced from the base. It is best to phase such pruning over a four-year period so that the plant continues to flower right through the exercise.

Malus (Eating and Crab-Apples) Nec/Pol T.

Apr-May, full sun

In the relatively sunny and dry areas of Britain, apple orchards are a common sight (as they are in many other temperate regions). Apples can be grown in more northern and wetter areas, and there are early and mid-season cultivars (as opposed to late), which make a showing under these conditions, but the increasing incidence of such diseases as canker, collar rot and scab make apple-growing a dubious commercial enterprise. The keen amateur is, however, a different kettle of fish and will persist in growing his or her favourite cultivars regardless of any such practical considerations.

Unlike many other plants, apples need to be cross-pollinated by another cultivar in order to produce good crops of fruit. For this to happen they must of course flower at around the same time. Some cultivars, such as 'Bramley's Seedling', produce pollen which is useless for

pollination, so if growing this cultivar *two* other cultivars are needed to ensure pollination of the Bramley and of each other. Usually, however, there will be sufficient pollinators (and these can be crab-apples) in suburban areas to ensure reasonable pollination without having to devote space to a second or third cultivar that you may not want.

The flowers are quite open and the nectar readily available to the bees, but it is also easily diluted by rain or heavy dews, reducing the sugar concentration to a level at which bees are not attracted.

For most small to average-sized gardens select your cultivars, grafted or budded, on dwarfing rootstocks such as M27, or semi-dwarfing such as M26, or the slightly more vigorous M9. This will ensure that your trees do not grow to enormous proportions, as many of them are capable of doing on more vigorous rootstocks. The choice of the form of the tree will be up to the individual, but where space is restricted the single-stemmed cordon, the flat-tiered espalier or aptly named fan are very suitable, especially where less vigorous rootstocks are used. Buy your trees ready trained unless you have lots of patience and a good deal of expertise! Crab-apples will not be trained, but still try to ensure that you have some idea of the ultimate size of the tree, which will of course depend on the rootstock: MM106 will give a larger tree than any of the rootstocks previously listed. Avoid the rootstock M9 for crab-apples, since trees grown on it will require permanent staking, which is acceptable for a 'cropping' tree but not for an ornamental one.

CRAB-APPLES

M. floribunda (Japanese Crab) ht: 15 ft *4.5 m* Apr. A real toffee-apple shaped tree, often wider than it is high, also very suitably grown as a shrub. The crimson buds which crown the arching branches open to a pinkish white and never fail, regardless of the season, to give a fabulous display. The fruits are not very showy.

'Golden Hornet' ht: 15 ft *4.5 m* Apr. White flowers followed by an abundance of yellow fruits that persist well into the new year.

'John Downie' ⬭ ht: 15 ft *4.5 m* Apr. Justifiably regarded as the best of the fruiting crabs, at least as far as its edible, bright orange-red conical fruits are concerned. The flowers are white.

'Profusion' ⬭ ht: 18 ft *5.5 m* Apr. The large wine-red and fragrant flowers are produced as the name suggests. The young leaves are purplish but change to a coppery red, which complements the small deep-red fruits perfectly; the fruit colour is more than skin deep and they look delicious — but are not. This is one of the few plants that I have ever seen attacked and severely tunnelled by the aptly named Leopard Moth.

'Red Jade' 🌲 ht: 12 ft *3.5 m* May. So named on account of its very persistent brilliantly red fruits, which follow the pink-white flowers.

M. sargentii ⬭ ht: 9 ft *3 m* Apr. This species is really more suitably grown as a shrub. The leaves are often distinctly three-lobed, and the flowers white with golden anthers. Very free-flowering. The bees love it and can be seen working the flowers in great number. Fruit bright red and cherry-like.

DESSERT AND CULINARY APPLES

If grown as cordons, space these at 2½ ft (75 cm), and if as fans or espaliers at 6-8 ft (2-2.5 m).

'Cox's Orange Pippin' Regarded by British fruit growers as the ultimate dessert apple, it does not do well under wet, relatively sunless conditions.

'Malling Kent' A possible alternative to Cox, and heavier cropping, less fussy and much easier to grow.

'Spartan' This variety grows well in my own garden in eastern Scotland, and I must say I prefer its flavour to that of Cox. But perhaps this is because I am not interested in breaking records for length of storage period, and prefer to eat my apples straight from the tree. The dark red skin polishes to a mirror-like shine and the white flesh tinged with green is as good to look at as it is to eat. In spite of my earlier comments it does store well, but like most cultivars is best eaten straight off the tree.

'Bramley's Seedling' There can be no argument over the fact that this is the finest culinary apple, and it is also a more than passable eater if stored. It tends to be rather vigorous, even on dwarfing rootstocks, so is best not grown as a cordon. The fruits are large and green, and some reddish-orange coloration is often present. The fruits store exceptionally well. Remember that if you decide you need pollinators, two will be required.

There is a host of other cultivars to tempt you, but try to taste the fruit before committing yourself for the next twenty years or so. If you really must try something different, then consider one of the so-called 'family trees', which have several cultivars on one rootstock.

Fruit-tree pruning is far too big a subject to deal with here, but try to prune every year, if only to thin crowded or crossing branches. It will be better than the sporadic scalpings to which most fruit trees are subjected.

Malva Nec/Pol H. ⚘

ht: 3 ft *90 cm* dist: 2 ft *60 cm*
Jun-Oct, full sun

A common name shared by two different genera of plants would suggest a fairly close botanical relationship. The marked visual similarity between species of *Malva* and *Lavatera* — both known as mallows — reinforces this, and with their masses of pollen both are equally attractive to the honey bee. *Malva* pollen is white, and the grains are some of the very largest known, having a diameter in excess of 1 mm: clearly visible to the naked eye.

Several species are found in the wild and some, such as *moschata* (Musk Mallow) are native to most of Europe. All are very easy to grow.

M. alcea Pink flowers 2-3 in (5-7.5 cm) across, leaves rounded at the base and variably divided above. The more upright form 'Fastigiata', which grows to 4 ft (1.2 m) is now frequently offered by seedsmen.

M. moschata Bright rose-purple flowers, up to 2 in (5 cm) in diameter. The leaves of this species are an added attraction, being deeply divided, rather like those of the cranesbills. The popular

Malva alcea, a mallow.

form 'Alba' has glistening white flowers and can be raised from seed.

Meconopsis Nec/Pol

semi-shade

Botanically the *Meconopsis* genus is nearly related to the poppies which they closely resemble. They do, however, need rather different growing conditions. A well drained soil with a good organic content with partial shelter is essential if they are to thrive.

M. betonicifolia (Himalayan Poppy) Bien. ht: 3 ft *90 cm* dist: 18 in *45 cm* Jun-Jul, acid. Once seen, these tall, brilliant blue poppies with their masses of yellow stamens are never forgotten. The mind's eye transports them immediately to some Tibetan hillside which is their true home. The individual flowers may be up to 2½ in (6.5 cm) in diameter, and there are usually several on each stem. The greyish-green leaves have very long stalks, 8-9 in (20-23 cm), with a 3-4 in

(7.5-10 cm) elliptic to oblong leaf blade which has flat notched lobes, not at all typical of the poppy family.

Strictly speaking this species is perennial, but it is rather short lived, so treat it as a biennial (see *M. regia* for details).

M. cambrica (Welsh Poppy) Bien. ht: 1 ft *30 cm* dist: 9 in *23 cm* Jun-Sep. This species has seeded itself around the British countryside and gardens very successfully, but I could never bring myself to pull even one of them out — the 1½ in (3.5 cm) yellow flowers are very fine. There is an orange form, 'Aurantiaca'.

M. grandis H. ht: 2 ft *60 cm* dist: 1 ft *30 cm* May-Jun. Variable but mostly blue flowers up to 4 in (10 cm) in diameter. The cultivar 'Branklyn' has more reliably blue flowers.

M. regia Bien. ht: 5 ft *1.5 m* dist: 2 ft *60 cm* May-Jun. The large yellow flowers are very showy, as are the magnificent 2 ft (60 cm) densely silver- or golden-haired, typical poppy-like leaves. Usually dies after flowering, so new plants should be raised each year.

Seed of all the species listed above (which just a few years ago was so difficult to obtain), and many others, is available from a number of seed firms. Good news for the bees, which work the flowers so avidly.

Melissa (Bee Balm) Nec/Pol H.

Jun-Sep, semi-shade

The white flowers are generally regarded as having too long a corolla tube for them to provide an easy nectar source for the honey bee, so it is not grown on this account alone, but on another.

The crinkly, scalloped nettle-like leaves are not only attractive, particularly in their yellow-green form, but they also have the most delicious lemon-scent. Bee Balm was used by the ancient skep beekeepers to rub on the inside of empty skeps to attract passing honey bee swarms into them — the original 'bait hives'. Recently it has been shown that the aromatic scents of the balm plant are the same as, or very similar to, those in Nasonov pheromone, which is fanned by the wings from a gland at the end of the abdomen and attracts other bees; it is used to collect stragglers and to guide the swarm into its new home. The ancient technique is, therefore, based on keen observation, and no doubt had some success.

M. officinalis 'Aurea' ht: 18 in *45 cm* dist: 12 in *30 cm* Golden leaves, continuous from spring to first frosts. Some light shade helps to prevent scorching of the foliage.

'Variegata' ht: 2 ft *60 cm* dist: 18 in *45 cm* Golden and green mottled leaves. No herb garden (or herbaceous border) should be without this superb plant.

* **Mentha** (Mint) Nec. H.
Aug-Oct, full sun, semi-shade
The flavour and fragrance of the various mints are universally known, but unfortunately it rarely grows in sufficient quantity, in any of its forms, to yield a large amount of the deliciously mint-flavoured honey.

The small four-lobed tubular flowers are carried in dense whorls, each flower enclosed at its base by a conspicuously veined and hairy five-pointed calyx.

In spite of their small size the flowers produce large quantities of nectar and are a particularly valuable late summer source. Unfortunately, the flowers are all too rarely seen in cultivation, the new growths being picked for various flavourings well before they reach the nectar stage. The more ornamental forms, with crinkly or variegated foliage, which are not normally used for flavouring, ironically produce very little in the way of flower. There are, however, many wild forms (and hybrids thereof) that flower freely, mostly in damp semi-shady areas.

Many of the mints are invasive and are often contained by planting in bottomless buckets or pipes, sunk to their rims to prevent the runners from spreading too much. You could use more vigorous neighbouring plants to help cure your mint's exuberance, but unless there is plenty of moisture in the soil the mint could end up suffering badly.

M. gentilis 'Variegata' (Ginger Mint) ht: 18 in *45 cm* dist: 12-18 in *30-45 cm* Nettle-like leaves heavily veined with gold, dark red stems and pale lilac flowers.

M. pulegium (Penny Royal) ht: 9 in *23 cm* dist: 12-18 in *30-45 cm* A good ground-cover plant, with small shiny green leaves. Freely produced lavender-coloured flowers. The whole plant is strongly aromatic.

* **Muscari** (Grape Hyacinth) Nec/Pol B/C.
ht: 5-9 in *12.5-23 cm* dist: 4-6 in *10-15 cm*
Mar-May, full sun, semi-shade
Muscari have a long flowering season and manage not only to look after themselves but also to extend their territory, even onto hard-packed gravel paths. This ability to grow virtually anywhere is perhaps less commonly seen now that persistent weedkillers are used so widely on paths and other 'odd corners'. The flower spikes are crowded with small, blue bell-shaped flowers ⅓ in long by ¼ in wide (8 x 6 mm), with a narrow petticoat of white around their fluted edges. The strong blue of *Muscari* looks well with dwarf narcissus and/or primroses. I have them growing near and through a dwarf white-flowered variegated *Arabis*, and this makes an attractive combination and gives dual interest for the bees. In fact, the plant appears to be much more attractive to honey bees than one might expect from its size and shape.

If you are worried about them spreading too much, cut off the flower spikes well before the seed is shed. Having plenty of space I tend not to worry about this, and I have the bonus of the dried silvery-brown flower spikes, rather like small versions of Honesty, right through the winter.

The flower scent is not unpleasant, but could be described as an acquired taste. Plant the bulbs about 3 in (7.5 cm) deep.

M. armeniacum Bright blue flowers on long spikes. The grass-like foliage is produced in autumn, long before the flower spikes. It can be invasive and will in time smother less vigorous alpines. Dwarf forms such as 'Cantab' may be available from specialist producers.

M. azureum A softer paler blue than other species.

M. botryoides Not highly rated by most gardeners, but its larger, more globular-shaped flowers make it a worthwhile addition. Not widely available, but it should prove easy enough to 'borrow' a few from a fellow beekeeper to get you started. The white form, *album*, which is less vigorous, is commonly grown on the rock garden.

* **Nemophila menziesii** Nec. A(h). ￦
ht: 6-8 in *15-20 cm* dist: 9 in *23 cm*
full sun, semi-shade
This is better known by its common name, 'Baby Blue Eyes'. The eye of the shallow, five-petalled, sky-blue flowers is in fact white. The stems are lax, and bear 2 in (5 cm) long leaves which are divided virtually to the central vein.

A very pleasant little plant, and quite attractive to bees, who forage for nectar and pollen, coming away with blue-grey loads on their legs.

* **Nepeta** (Catmint or Catnip) Nec/Pol H.
￦
Jun-Sep, dry, full sun
If you already have catmint in your garden and would like to know its correct generic or cultivar name, you may have problems. The nomenclature seems to be rather confused, and there is no doubt that there are a fair number of seed-raised hybrids around, often self-sown, that have found their way into cultivation, thus adding to the confusion. However, all the plants that I have seen are equally attractive to bees, there being literally hundreds of individual two-lipped flowers on even a small plant.

Cats adore the smell and will devastate your plants by chewing, scratching and rolling all over them, and will return for a regular fix! Catmints are, however, pretty tough and will usually win through. Most people find the smell verging on the offensive, but if you do not get too close you cannot fail to be won over by its very long flowering season and pretty blue flowers carried on long spikes, complemented by grey or green toothed leaves. An excellent bee plant.

Tidy the plants by cutting down to ground level in the autumn.

N. x faassenii ht: 18 in *45 cm* dist: 2 ft *60 cm* Leaves grey and downy, flowers pale lavender. Does not produce seed.

N. gigantea 'Six Hills Giant' ht: 2½-3 ft *75-90 cm* dist: 3 ft *90 cm* An altogether more vigorous plant; leaves greener and flowers violet-blue, lower lip frilled and spotted.

Nigella damascena (Love-in-a-Mist) Nec/Pol A(h). ￦
ht: 18 in *45 cm* dist: 9 in *23 cm*
Jun-Oct, full sun
The common name most aptly describes the impression given by this rather elegant plant, with its feathery leaves and epicalyxes surrounding the solitary terminal flowers. As the buds open, the 'ruff' is pushed outwards to reveal the five or six pointed petals. The flower really is quite beautiful and has a mass of stamens from which emerge five or six writhing pistils. The dozen or so nectaries, which sit at the base of the petals, look rather like a black cow's head with two dark shiny eyes and a long nose, complete with eyebrows and nasal hair! The 'nose' separates to give access to the bag-like nectar store, which is well protected from the elements.

Seed is usually sown in situ in March, and dwarf cultivars are now starting to come on to the market. When the flowers are over, the inflated seed pods dry very well and are frequently seen in winter flower arrangements.

'Miss Jekyll' Cornflower blue.

'Persian Jewels' An interesting mixture of blue, mauve, purple, pink and white flowers.

Oenothera (Evening Primrose) Pol.
Jun-Sep, dry, full sun
In spite of their common name most of the species open their flowers by day. Pollination, however, is not achieved until the evening, when long-tongued moths take the nectar from the deep narrow flower tube into which the four rather flat petals are fused, and all are

Nepeta — cat amongst the catnip.

yellow unless otherwise stated. The sepals, which are fused with the flower tube, are often of a different colour, frequently dull red or pink. It is not uncommon to see *Oenothera* naturalized by the roadside, particularly on waste or recently disturbed ground, and they do make ideal plants for a hot dry location.

The pollen grain of *Oenothera* is shaped like a 'Y', with equal length limbs and angles, and it also has several long threads growing from the centre part of the grain. Honey bees work the flowers for pollen, but find it almost impossible to pack it in their 'pollen baskets', at least tidily, so one sees them coming away from the plant trailing a ribbon of tangled pollen grains from their legs.

O. biennis (Evening Primrose) Bien. ht: 3 ft *90 cm* dist: 2 ft *60 cm* Jun-Sep. 'The' evening primrose. Flowers 1½ in (3.5 cm) across on slender spikes.

O. caespitosa H. ht: 6 in *15 cm* dist: 12 in *30 cm* Jun-Sep. One for the rock garden or scree bed. Pure white flowers 2½ in (6.5 cm) across.

O. missouriensis H. ht: 9 in *23 cm* dist: 12-18 in *30-45 cm* The shallow bowl-shaped flowers, 4 in (10 cm) across, are quite superb on this rather dwarf sprawling plant. Waxy leaves.

O. tetragona 'Fireworks' H. ht: 18 in *45 cm* dist: 12 in *30 cm* Jun-Sep. A very colourful plant with purplish leaves and red flower buds.

Olearia (Daisy Bush) Nec/Pol Shr.

dry, salt tol, full sun

What an apt common name this is for these most easily grown Australasian shrubs, which thrive in dry soils and tolerate any amount of sun. In season they are literally smothered with the white, many-petalled, single chrysanthemum-like flowers. The leaves are usually grey or grey-green and quite leathery. They are

107

unfortunately not reliably hardy except in milder coastal districts, so if you live inland and wish to preserve your stock take a few of the easily rooted cuttings each year in August, for you will probably lose your plants about one year in four or five, but they do grow quickly.

O. x haastii ht: 6 ft *2 m* dist: 4-5 ft *1.25-1.5 m* Jun-Jul. By far the hardiest, and worth trying even in cold areas. The fragrant flowers are produced very freely, leaves dark green above, grey felted beneath.

O. macrodonta ht: 8 ft *2.5 m* dist: 6-7 ft *2-2.25 m* Jun-Jul. Handsome sage-green holly-like leaves, silvery-white felted beneath. Masses of fragrant flowers carried in rounded 6 in (15 cm) clusters.

* **Origanum** (Marjoram) Nec/Pol
full sun
Best known for its culinary properties, there are also some very ornamental species, all of which produce nectar copiously from the small distinctly two-lipped flowers. The flowers of all species have tubular bases, but many of the most ornamental ones are far too long for honey bees to penetrate, so care must be taken when choosing your plants.

O. marjorana (Sweet or Knotted Marjoram) Ann. ht: 2 ft *60 cm* dist: 18 in *45 cm* Jul-Sep. This is best treated as an annual in the British climate, although strictly speaking it is a perennial. The leaves are strongly aromatic and this is 'the' marjoram for cooking purposes. Remember that if you use too many shoots or leaves, the flowers (inconspicuous but very attractive to bees) will be few and far between.

O. rotundifolium H. ht: 9 in *23 cm* dist: 18 in *45 cm* Aug-Oct. Glaucous leaves and pink flowers almost obscured by the drooping clusters of pale green, hop-like bracts. Not reliably hardy.

O. vulgare H. ht: 12 in *30 cm* dist: 12 in *30 cm* Jul-Sep. In spite of its name this is a very attractive plant, especially in the wild, growing in short grass in any dryish soil throughout Europe. It is worked very enthusiastically by bees.

The flower stems are reddish, as are the buds in the clustered flower heads before they open to white. There is always a good mixture of buds and flowers, making this a very pretty plant indeed. In the wild, on the alkaline soils where this plant is plentiful, its nectar is converted into a strong mint-flavoured honey which is delicious. Unfortunately, as with many of the plant essential oils, the fine aromatic flavour of Marjoram honey will only be found when freshly extracted, as it is lost during crystallization.

Osmanthus Nec/Pol Shr.
full sun
The clusters of small, white, four-petalled flowers are not particularly striking, but are plentiful and show up well against the dark evergreen leaves, and they are beautifully scented, rather reminiscent of Jasmine.

O. delavayi ht: 7 ft *2.25 m* dist: 7 ft *2.25 m* Apr-May. By far the most commonly planted species, with finely toothed leaves.

O. heterophyllus ht: 10 ft *3 m* dist: 8-10 ft *2.5-3 m* Sep-Oct. Rather variable, prickly, holly-like leaves which may be up to 3 in (7.5 cm) long. The golden and white variegated forms, 'Aureomarginatus' and 'Variegatus' respectively, are both showy and, as with all such plants, are slower growing.

* **Papaver** (Poppy) Pol.
full sun
The cornfield poppy, familiar to all because of its association with Remembrance Day, has virtually disappeared from the landscape, largely due to changes in farming practices, such as the widespread use of herbicides and the grubbing out of hedgerows. The genus does, however, contain many other species, large and small, annual and perennial, in a wide range of very showy colours, all of which (with the exception of double-flowered cultivars) bear large amounts of pollen. This is blue-black in the field poppy, but usually greenish-yellow in other species. Poppy pollen is extremely attractive to the honey bee, which will search out the flowers wherever they occur.

All the single poppies are great providers of pollen.

The mass of stamens surround a barrel-shaped pistil surmounted by a large ribbed stigma. The whole structure swells to become the familiar poppy seed head, which is so widely used in dried flower arrangements.

There are usually four or six petals of a satiny texture, and as they are unsupported by sepals (which fall early) they are in constant motion in even the slightest breeze. Most poppies seed themselves very freely, so unless you are prepared for an invasion cut the seed heads off before they have time to mature.

The foliage is variable but is usually much divided and in some species hairy.

P. alpinum H. ht: 9 in *23 cm* dist: 9 in *23 cm* May-Aug. Flowers usually bright yellow (but white, pink and orange forms also occur), and up to 1½ in (3.5 cm) in diameter. The leaves are blue-green and much divided. A marvellous little alpine plant for the rock garden or scree.

P. commutatum 'Ladybird' A(h). ht: 18 in *45 cm* dist: 9 in *23 cm* Jun-Oct. A real show-stopper, with brilliant red petals each of which has a jet black spot.

P. nudicaule (Iceland Poppy) Bien. ht: 2 ft *60 cm* dist: 18 in *45 cm* Jun-Oct. These large, 2½ in (6.5 cm), fragrant flowers have a fabulous pastel colour range. The cultivar 'Champagne Bubbles'

is rather less vigorous and has attractively crinkled petals. Although it is a perennial it is not a long-lived one, so is best treated as an annual or biennial. It is also the only poppy suitable for use as a cut flower, since it does not drop its petals as freely as other species. Plant them at the edges of borders of herbaceous plants or other annuals.

P. orientale H. May-Jun. The giant of the group, both with regard to height and its massive 6 in (15 cm) flowers — a statuesque and very showy plant. The leaves are long, dark green and bristly. Unless they are grown in good light, without shade, the flowering stems will need some support, but this weakness can be overcome to a certain extent by choosing one of the less vigorous cultivars. Ideal plants for the mixed shrub or herbaceous border.

'Allegro' ht: 18 in *45 cm* dist: 18-24 in *45-60 cm* Scarlet flowers on short stems.

'Goliath' ht: 4 ft *1.25 m* dist: 3 ft *1 m* Scarlet flowers on tall stems.

'Mrs Perry' ht: 3 ft *1 m* dist: 2 ft *60 cm* Salmon pink flowers.

'Perry's White' ht: 3 ft *90 cm* dist: 2 ft *60 cm* Pure white flowers.

Bee plants — Philadelphus

P. rhoeas 'The Shirley' Ann. ht: 12-18 in *30-45 cm* dist: 9 in *23 cm* Jun-Aug. A strain of mixed colours of the field poppy, in shades of red, pink and white, which looks very well amongst other bright-flowered hardy annuals.

* **Philadelphus** (Mock Orange) Nec/Pol Shr.
𝄞 ☁
Jun-Jul, full sun, semi-shade
As an easily grown summer-flowering shrub yielding both nectar and pollen, the *Philadelphus* has few equals. The white flowers are produced in profusion and have the delicious heady fragrance of orange-blossom. However, left to their own devices they tend to become very large plants, up to 15 ft (4.5 m) high and as much across. This exuberance can to some extent be controlled by judicious pruning, but it is far better to choose one of the many excellent less vigorous cultivars, so that pruning can be kept to an absolute minimum, for remember that all pruning actually reduces the total number of flowers.

The growth habit is intensely twiggy, with new shoots being produced from the suckering rootstock.

The clusters of four-petalled flowers, which may be up to 2 in (5 cm) in diameter, have a mass of yellow stamens.

'Beauclerk' ht: 6 ft *2 m* dist: 4 ft *1.25 m* This cultivar has the largest flowers, well over 2 in (5 cm) in diameter.

P. coronarius 'Aureus' ht: 4 ft *1.25 m* dist: 3 ft *1 m* Not as free-flowering as the species, but the golden-green leaves are beautiful. This cultivar needs a sheltered spot, otherwise the leaves will scorch.

P. microphyllus ht: 3 ft *1 m* dist: 2 ft *60 cm* A gem of a plant, with small leaves and strongly scented flowers.

Phlox Pol.
The narrow flower tubes of both the herbaceous and alpine phlox are too long for nectar (which in any case is only produced in small quantities) to be collected by the honey bee. The colour range in both types is, however, superb and

The sweetly scented Philadelphus 'Beauclerk' is a very rewarding shrub to have in the garden.

they are commonly seen in most gardens. The alpine types bear their five-petalled flowers in spring or early summer, the herbaceous types in autumn. All have five accessible anthers bearing bright yellow pollen.

ALPINE TYPES 🌿 🎋
The leaves are generally small and lance-shaped, obscured completely by sheets of flower during the relatively short but splendid flowering period.

P. adsurgans ht: 9 in *23 cm* dist: 12-18 in *30-45 cm* Jun, acid, semi-shade. Shiny leaves and ¾ in (2 cm) shell-pink flowers with a deeper eye.

P. amoena 'Variegata' ht: 5 in *12.5 cm* dist: 12 in *30 cm* May-Jun, full sun. Attractively variegated foliage with vivid pink flowers up to 1 in (2.5 cm) across.

P. douglasii ht: 5 in *12.5 cm* dist: 18-24 in *45-60 cm* May, full sun, semi-shade. This forms large mats of rather straggly foliage, bearing pretty ⅔ in (1.5 cm) diameter flowers. Blue, white and pink cultivars are commonly available.

P. subulata ht: 5 in *12.5 cm* dist: 2-3 ft *60-90 cm* May, full sun. Even more invasive than *douglasii*, but it is easy to forgive such a fabulously free-flowering plant. Just remember to chop back (short back and sides) as soon as the flowering period is over. Cultivars in a wide range of colours are available, the most striking of which is perhaps 'Temiscaming', with its vivid cerise flowers. 'G.F. Wilson' is pale blue, more subtle, and well worth growing.

HERBACEOUS TYPES H. ⚘ ht: 3-4 ft *1-1.25 m* dist: 2 ft *60 cm* Aug-Oct, full sun

P. paniculata Fragrant 1 in (2.5 cm) flowers in dense, rounded, pyramidal clusters above narrow pointed 4 in (10 cm) leaves. The flowers last longer and fade less if grown in light shade. The colour range is wide — white to red and red-violet, with all the intermediate tints.

'Harlequin' Purple flowers and handsomely yellow variegated foliage.

'White Admiral' White flowers.

'Starfire' Deep glowing red.

Potentilla Nec/Pol

There are two distinct types of potentilla: the shrubby types with persistent stems, and the herbaceous ones.

SHRUBBY TYPES (Shrubby Cinquefoils) Shr. ⚘ ⚘ Jun-Nov, full sun, semi-shade

The exceptionally long flowering season, coupled with the profusion of flowers, most commonly lemon or bright yellow, make the mound-like potentillas most valuable garden plants. The flowers, carried singly or in clusters, are around 1¼ in (3 cm) and are quite flat, allowing easy bee access. The five rounded petals overlap and the colour is less intense on the underside. The flower buds, stems and conspicuous dark-brown stipules are distinctly hairy. Leaves are variable in size, smaller than the flowers, with 3-5 narrow leaflets divided to the base.

A wide range is available — over fifty in fact,

but it would be difficult to make a bad choice. No more than three or four will, however, be on offer in the average garden centre.

P. arbuscula 'Beesii' ht: 3 ft *90 cm* dist: 2 ft *60 cm* The branchlets of the *arbuscula* cultivars are typically shaggy in appearance due to the longer stipules, which are very conspicuous. The golden flowers cover the mounded silvery foliage for most of the summer and autumn.

P. fruticosa 'Elizabeth' ht: 3 ft *90 cm* dist: 2 ft *60 cm* Flowers of rich yellow set off to perfection by the very dainty foliage. An excellent plant.

'Goldfinger' ht: 3 ft *90 cm* dist: 2 ft *60 cm* Has perhaps the largest, deepest golden flowers of all the potentillas, whilst 'Gold-digger' and 'Klondike' have similar flowers but are a shade paler. 'Klondike' also has much more delicate foliage.

'Katherine Dykes' ht: 5 ft *1.5 m* dist: 3 ft *90 cm* A vigorous and very widely grown cultivar with an abundance of primrose-coloured flowers.

'Longacre' ht: 3 ft *1 m* dist: 2 ft *60 cm* Similar to 'Elizabeth' but rather more dwarf, with darker foliage and more slender branches.

'Mandshurica' ht: 1 ft *30 cm* dist: 9 in *23 cm* A real little charmer, with white flowers on silvery foliage. Ideal for a sunny spot on the rock garden.

'Princess' ht: 3 ft *1 m* dist: 2 ft *60 cm* With its pink to pale-pink flowers, 'Princess' looks rather like a dwarf thornless dog-rose. A very pretty plant that justifiably sells extremely well.

'Red Ace' ht: 3 ft *1 m* dist: 2 ft *60 cm* Regarded as a breakthrough by some and an abomination by others, its bright colour has ensured that it is now widely grown. See it in flower before you decide.

'Tangerine' ht: 3 ft *1 m* dist: 2 ft *60 cm* Although this plant has a reputation for shyness of flowering it is as profuse in my garden as any other cultivar I have seen. The colour is even and deep, but I do grow it in light shade and this helps to prevent the flowers fading. Flanked on either side by *Anchusa* and *Nepeta* with their blue flowers, the contrast looks good and the bees like all three plants.

HERBACEOUS PLANTS (Cinquefoils) H. ⚘ Jun-Oct, dry, full sun, semi-shade

Pleasant enough border plants but coarser in leaf, flower and form than their shrubby counterparts. The double and semi-double flowered types are not at all attractive to my eye or to the honey bee and are not mentioned here. The single-flowered cultivars which are 18 in (45 cm) or so in height are good bee plants and are useful for border edging.

P. atrosanguinea 'Gibsons Scarlet' ht: 12-18 in *30-45 cm* dist: 12 in *30 cm* A very old cultivar that has deservedly retained its popularity. The sprays of blood-red flowers have a darker eye, and look well with the dark green foliage.

P. nepalensis 'Miss Willmott' ht: 12 in *30 cm* dist: 9-12 in *23-30 cm* Similar in form to 'Gibsons Scarlet' but with deep pink flowers with a red eye.

'Roxana' ht: 12 in *30 cm* dist: 9-12 in *23-30 cm* Flowers two-toned orange and scarlet.

P. anserina (Silverweed) An attractive creeping plant with leaves shaped rather like the wild briar, but soft and silkily hairy, particularly on the undersides, and yellow flowers about ¾ in (2 cm) in diameter. Commonly found by roadsides or waste ground, often growing well in damp heavy soils. It can be invasive and there are perhaps not too many gardeners/ beekeepers who would wish to introduce it to their carefully maintained gardens!

* **Prunus** Nec/Pol ⚘
Japanese flowering cherries are what most people think of whenever Prunus cherries are mentioned, but the genus is far more diverse than this and includes the apricots, peaches, plums (including gages, damsons and bullaces), bird cherries, almonds, laurels (common and Portuguese) and, of course, the 'eating cherries'. In cooler climates such as Britain, the fruiting peaches and apricots are really non-starters, but all the others can do very well indeed.

Most of the cherries flower early and so provide a valuable early nectar source, provided frost does not damage the flowers and it is mild enough for it to be produced.

For ease of reference I have divided the cherries into six groups.

EVERGREEN LAURELS Shr. ◯ full sun, semi-shade

P. laurocerasus (Common or Cherry Laurel) ht: 20 ft *6 m* dist: 15 ft *4.5 m* Apr, acid. A large wide-spreading shrub with handsome, leathery 6-7 in (15-18 cm) leaves with conspicuous yellow-green venation, dull pale-green beneath. The plants grow far too large for most gardens, unless grown as a hedge, for which they are very suitable.

If unclipped they flower very freely, the 6 in (15 cm) 'candles' being very similar to those of *P. padus*, but erect. In addition to the flowers the undersides of the younger leaves have extra-floral nectaries which attract bees right through the summer, and especially at times when nectar is scarce elsewhere.

Many good cultivars are available, and some of the slender flower candles are followed by small red fruits which eventually turn to a dark purple. Less rampant ones are listed below.

'Otto Luyken' ht: 4 ft *1.25 m* dist: 4 ft *1.25 m* Apr. Very much smaller and narrower leaves than the species, but the flower spikes are just about the same size. A long-standing favourite of mine in its own right, but also as a contrast to more showy plants.

'Zabeliana' ht: 4 ft *1.25 m* dist: 6 ft *2 m* Apr. Rather less compact than 'Otto Luyken' and also rather more graceful, with its slightly lax branches and longer willow-like leaves.

P. lusitanica (Portuguese Laurel) ht: 15 ft *4.5 m* dist: 10 ft *3 m* Jun. A handsome plant with ovate leaves which are considerably smaller and darker green than those of *laurocerasus*. The petioles and young twigs are a deep burgundy and are a distinct and attractive feature. A much slower grower than *laurocerasus*.

The less-vigorous variegated form 'Variegata' is even more handsome, with its leaf margins irregularly splotched with white. Some pink coloration may also be in evidence on young growths, especially during the winter period.

Coming in to land, a honey bee approaches Prunus laurocerasus 'Otto Luyken'. One is much more likely to see this in flower than the common laurel, which is so often pruned back.

PLUMS T. ⅄ 🔎 ht: 12 ft *3.5 m* Apr, full sun

These can form very large trees, so try to obtain them on the rootstock 'Pixy', which should limit your tree's height to 12 ft (3.5 m) or so, and bring them into fruit more quickly than the traditional rootstocks. Alternatively, grow them on a wall as a fan or espalier, especially if shelter from cold winds is likely to be a problem. Both the varieties described below are self-fertile and require no pollination. Both are also prone to the bacterial disease Silver Leaf, for which there is no control other than cutting back the branches well beyond the infected area, taking care to sterilize your secateurs afterwards with household bleach. It is best to seek expert advice before hacking back 'innocent' plants, since the leaves of some cultivars have a naturally silver appearance. Carry out any pruning that is necessary between March and June so that wounds heal quickly.

'Czar' culinary. A cultivar with beautiful blue-purple 'bloomy' fruits. If allowed to ripen well it is also a good eater.

'Victoria' The best and most reliable cropping dessert plum in the British climate. The fruits are large, egg-shaped and yellow flushed with deep scarlet.

FRUITING CHERRIES T. ⅄ 🌿 ht: 12 ft *3.5 m* Apr, full sun

Together with the 'flowering' cherries the fruiting types provide the highest nectar concentration levels of any of the *Prunus*, with the exception of the laurels. In fact, cherry orchards will provide a considerable honey crop in many seasons. The cherries have extra-floral nectaries in the form of two small lumps on the side of the leaf petiole just below the leaf blade.

'Stella' This is a self-fertile cultivar that produces large dark-red heart-shaped fruits even

113

Bee plants — Prunus

in the more northerly regions of Britain. Again the rootstock 'Pixy' is the best choice for the average-sized garden. They can be grown as free-standing trees or on a wall as an espalier or fan, which will give a measure of protection and encourage bees to visit the flowers.

FLOWERING CHERRIES T. ⅄ Apr, full sun

What an enormous choice there is of these lovely trees that flower so profusely that they look like pink, white or cream clouds against a blue spring sky. Make certain that you are buying single-flowered or semi-double culti-vars, since double-flowered ones are more likely to be commonly available.

'Amanogawa' ⅄ ht: 30 ft *9 m* The most upright of the flowering cherries, rather like a Lombardy Poplar but covered with fragrant pale-pink semi-double flowers. Its form makes it ideal for confined spaces. For a really superb combination 'Amanogawa' is sometimes grafted at a height of 5-6 ft (1.5-1.8 m) on to the glossy stems of *P. serrula* (see below).

'Hisakura' ⅄ ht: 20 ft *6 m* Single, or sometimes semi-double, deep-pink flowers and attractive coppery-red young leaves.

'Shirotae' ⅂⅂ ht: 20 ft *6 m* Flowers white, fragrant, single or semi-double, carried in long drooping clusters. The leaves are distinctly 'toothed'.

'Tai Haku' (Great White Cherry) ⅂⅂ ht: 35 ft *10.5 m* The common name fits this magnificent tree well. There is a group of them at Dartington Hall in Devon, standing close to tall dark green yew hedges against which they are just breath-taking when in full flower. They are, however, wide spreading trees (30-40 ft *9-12 m*) and they do cast deep shade, so are not really suitable for any but the largest of gardens. New growth is coppery.

ORNAMENTAL ALMONDS T. ⅄ Mar, full sun

Even earlier flowering than the cherries, but most cultivars are not as showy.

P. dulcis 'Alba' ⬭ ht: 12-15 ft *3.5-4.5 m* White single flowers.

The delicate pink-tinged Prunus 'Amanogawa'. The bee is probably collecting nectar.

'Erecta' ⅄ ht 18 ft *5.5 m* Its erect habit makes it more suitable for small gardens. Pink flowers.

P. x amygdalo-persica 'Pollardii' ⬭ ht: 20 ft *6 m* This is a cross between peach and almond, and it has larger, deeper pink flowers than any of the other almonds.

OTHER DECIDUOUS CHERRIES T. ⅄ full sun

P. avium (Gean, Mazzard or Wild Cherry) ⬭ ht: 30 ft *9 m* Mar-Apr. Certainly one of the showiest of our native flowering trees, widely distributed throughout Europe and with smaller, more delicate white flowers than some of its more vulgar Japanese counterparts. The trees literally 'hum' with bees during flowering. The small dull red fruits are pleasant enough to eat, but hardly provide a feast. The autumn leaf colour is usually good and is complemented by grey-red fissured bark in older trees. There is also a weeping cultivar, 'Pendula'.

P. cerasifera 'Pissardii' (Purple-leaved Plum) ⬭ ht: 25 ft *7.5 m* Mar-Apr. A small tree with dark red foliage which turns a deeper purple as it ages. More commonly grown in Britain as a hedging plant, but elsewhere in Europe it is a fairly common street tree, and very showy. Flowers pale pink.

'Cistena' see section on hedging.

P. x hillieri 'Spire' ht: 20 ft *6 m* Mar-Apr. Flowers pale pink; good autumn leaf colour. An ideal tree for the average-sized garden.

P. padus (Bird Cherry) ht: 40 ft *12 m* May-Jun. The small, white almond-scented flowers with yellowish 'eyes' are grouped together in slender drooping 6 in (15 cm) candles — like small versions of the horse-chestnut and those of the evergreen cherry laurels. The bark is a very dark brown turning black with age. The fruits too are black. Widely distributed throughout most of Europe.

The cultivar 'Waterii' has 8-9 in (20-23 cm) candles and is well worth growing if you have the space.

P. sargentii ht: 30 ft *9 m* Mar. As good to look at in autumn, with its lovely leaf coloration of reds and oranges, as it is in spring with its pink flowers and coppery new growth. One of the very best garden trees.

P. serrula ht: 30 ft *9 m* May. Grown principally for its brilliant shiny red-brown bark, it can nevertheless be free-flowering, but as the flowers are small, white and unremarkable (and partially hidden by the leaves), they often pass largely unnoticed except by the bees.

P. spinosa (Blackthorn or Sloe) ht: 15 ft *4.5 m* Mar-May. Very common in hedgerows throughout Europe. The purple-leaved cultivar 'Purpurea' is a fine shrub/tree and is well worth growing. The plant is usually of little use to the honey bee as it flowers in the 'blackthorn winter', but in a warm season the bees will obtain some very useful early pollen. It is doubtful if they ever get much nectar. The bitter blue-black fruits have a white waxy bloom.

P. subhirtella 'Autumnalis' ht: 15 ft *4.5 m* Nov-Mar. Some of the small, whitish, semi-double flowers may be present from November to March. The twigs bearing the flowers are rather thin and lax, and the plant needs a dark background to show off the flowers to their best advantage.

P. x yedoensis ht: 30 ft *9 m* Mar. Very early flowering, with a profusion of pale pink, almond-scented flowers.

Pulmonaria (Lungwort) Pol. H.
ht: 1 ft *30 cm* dist: 1 ft *30 cm*
Jan-May, semi-shade
Not in the first rank of bee plants, as the nectar, which is freely produced even on cold days in shady situations, is inaccessible at the bottom of the flower tube. The 1/3 in (8 mm) flowers funnel out above the calyx into five rounded pinky-blue petals, with five stamens alternating with short tufts of hair clustered round the throat of the funnel, guarding access to the tube itself.

The hairy leaves are, in some species, heavily spotted with white, and this is an attractive and distinctive feature.

P. angustifolia An unspotted species with bright blue flowers.

'Munstead Blue' As above, but dwarfer and very slightly later flowering.

P. officinalis This species, which is native to most of Europe, usually but not always has spotted leaves.

P. saccharata A handsome plant with white-spotted leaves and pinky-blue flowers.

'Argentea' A silver-leaved form.

'Pink Dawn' A pink-flowered form.

All pulmonarias do well on moist soil well supplied with organic matter, and being ground-huggers are less liable to wind damage than taller plants, and manage to attract a few bees if little pollen is available from other sources.

* **Pyracantha** (Firethorn) Nec/Pol Shr.
ht: 10-12 ft *3-3.5 m* dist: 8-10 ft *2.5-3 m*
May-Jun, salt tol, full sun, semi-shade
A rather stiff, angular shrub that bears large clusters of hawthorn-like white flowers, followed by even larger clusters of 1/4 in (6 mm) bright red, yellow or orange fruits which last well on into winter. Although closely related to the cotoneasters, the firethorns are to my mind

more showy and distinctive, with their gaunt form, dark green toothed leaves and spiny stems.

Under suitably warm conditions nectar is profusely produced from the masses of flowers that usually cover the firethorns from head to toe in late spring.

All pyracanthas are very shade-tolerant, and grow successfully even on north or east-facing walls. Being non-climbers, horizontal wires a foot (30 cm) or more apart will be required to tie in the vigorous upright branches. Choose five or six branches to cover the wall, and tie them in as their growth progresses. Cut back all side shoots to 2-3 in (5-7.5 cm) immediately after flowering, as this will encourage the 'stumps' to form fruiting spurs for the following year and give a clear view of the newly formed fruit clusters.

Allow a space of at least 9 ft x 9 ft (2.7 x 2.7 m) for any pyracantha grown as a wall shrub. Those grown on a south-facing wall are far more likely to be visited by bees. Unfortunately, like cotoneasters, pyracanthas are prone to fireblight. For details of this disease and recommendations, see *Cotoneaster*.

Make certain that you purchase container-grown plants.

'Orange Charmer' Very free-fruiting, with clusters of small orange fruits.

'Mojave' Large orange-red berries. Said to be more resistant to the depredations of birds and to fireblight.

'Wateri' Less vigorous than many other cultivars, with bright red fruits.

Rhododendron Nec. Shr. ⬭

acid, semi-shade

Few plants, with the possible exception of the rose, have captured the gardening public's imagination more than the rhododendrons (Rose Tree), with their great showy clusters of flowers and dark green leathery leaves. Consequently there are literally thousands of species and hybrids to choose from, many of which are far too large for the average garden.

In spite of their popularity they are not ideal garden plants, for an acid soil is always required

and the flowering season is relatively short. In addition, rhododendrons have of old had a reputation for producing poisonous nectar — poisonous to both bees and then to humans in the form of the honey made from it. Traditionally, this related to *R. ponticum*, although more recently *R. thomsonii* has been known to kill colonies collecting it. Upon investigation, the poison andromedotoxin was found to be responsible. If one rhododendron can produce this poison, it is perhaps also produced by others, but there may well be degrees of poisoning depending on the concentration in the nectar. The honey bee, however, works a range of rhododendrons, mostly for nectar, and appears unharmed from my own observations. Whatever poison there may be would be so diluted under normal 'mixed' garden conditions that it is very unlikely to ever be a serious problem. Large estates with heavy concentrations of rhododendrons may well be a different story, particularly in hot dry summers when the nectar is unusually concentrated.

SPECIES AND THEIR HYBRIDS ⬭

R. augustinii ht: 8 ft *2.5 m* dist: 6 ft *2 m* Apr-May. Small-leaved, with beautiful clear blue flowers. It is a good idea to see the plants in flower before purchasing since there are many inferior purplish-flowered forms in cultivation.

Definitely one of the best rhododendrons for the medium to large garden.

R. campylogynum ht: 1 ft *30 cm* dist: 2 ft *60 cm* Apr-May. Small shiny leaves with deep purplish-brown, waxy, bell-shaped flowers.

R. impeditum ht: 9 in *23 cm* dist: 18 in *45 cm* Apr-May. An ideal plant for the rock garden, with tiny aromatic leaves and bluish-purple, funnel-shaped flowers. Slow grower.

R. scintillans ht: 2 ft *60 cm* dist: 2 ft *60 cm* Apr-May. Small-leaved, with small lavender-blue funnel-shaped flowers.

R. yakushimanum ht: 3 ft *1 m* dist: 3 ft *1 m* Apr-May. I first saw this most beautiful of all the larger-flowered dwarf rhododendrons in the mid 60s, and was immediately captivated by its dense rounded habit and clusters of rose-pink

Rhododendron 'Lady Rosebery', one of the
most beautiful hybrids.

flower buds which open to the palest appleblossom pink. Once sufficient numbers come
on to the market this species is likely to be the
number one choice for most gardeners, since it
has the form and flower of the larger hybrids
without their embarrassing size. There are a
number of cultivars with flowers ranging from
white to red.

The number of hybrid rhododendrons available is legion. Choose them with care, particularly with regard to their ultimate size, and
remember that a border filled with them will be
a pretty sombre spectacle for ten months of the
year.

'Blue Diamond' ht: 3 ft *1 m* dist: 3 ft *1 m* Apr-
May. Lavender-blue flowers, aromatic foliage.

'Chikor' ht: 18 in *45 cm* dist: 2 ft *60 cm* Apr-May.
Small leaves and freely-produced bright yellow
flowers.

'Doncaster' ht: 4 ft *1.25 m* dist: 4 ft *1.25 m* Apr-
May. Funnel-shaped, crimson-scarlet flowers
with black markings inside, and dark green
leaves.

'Jenny' ht: 9 in *23 cm* dist: 2 ft *60 cm* Apr-May. A
real ground-hugger, with deep red, bell-shaped
flowers. If rhododendron nectar is poisonous
then 'Jenny' should be a killer, for large
quantities of nectar are produced at the bases of
the deep red bell-shaped flowers. However, the
honey bees which eagerly work the flowers
appear not to be harmed by it.

'Scarlet Wonder' ht: 2 ft *60 cm* dist: 2 ft *60 cm*
Apr-May. Trumpet-shaped flowers with frilly
petals.

The hybrids 'Britannia' (crimson-scarlet),
'Cynthia' (rose-crimson), 'Pink Pearl' and
'Purple Splendour' are all ultimately too large
for most gardens, but will no doubt continue to
be grown, for they are irresistible when in full
flower and are commonly available.

117

Azalea 'Golden Oriole', a deep Chinese-yellow with an orange blotch on the petals.

AZALEAS

The azaleas, as they are known (and will no doubt continue to be known by everyone except the botanists) are, in fact, also classified as rhododendrons. These are, to my mind, much more suitable for the average to small garden, since they are usually in scale with it, averaging around 3-5 ft (90-150 cm) in height. There are both deciduous and evergreen types.

DECIDUOUS AZALEAS ht: 5 ft *1.5 m* dist: 5 ft *1.5 m* May-Jun

There are several groups to choose from, and a wide range of cultivars in each.

'Gloria Mundi' Bright orange flowers, an unbelievable sight when in full flower.

'Kosters Brilliant Red' A deservedly very popular cultivar.

'Cecile' Deep pink, becoming paler as it opens, with yellow in the flared throat.

'Lemonora' Deep apricot-yellow, with a red tinge on the outside.

'Satan' Blood-red flowers with a trace of yellow staining at the base of the petals.

EVERGREEN AZALEAS ht: 3 ft *1 m* dist: 3-4 ft *1-1.25 m* Apr-May.

There are a large number of groups of evergreens and a bewildering choice of cultivars and colours, all of which flower very profusely, so your choice should be an easy one.

'Addy Werry' Deep vermilion red.

'Blaauws Pink' Salmon pink with paler shading.

'Hinodegiri' Bright crimson.

'Orange Beauty' Salmon-orange.

'Palestrina' A real cracker, with crowds of white flowers with the palest of apple-green eyes. If you have space for just one cultivar, then make it this one.

'Vuyks Scarlet' Bright red with frilled petals.

* **Ribes** Nec/Pol Shr. 〰 ⬚
full sun, semi-shade
This undemanding, large and varied genus contains the common (but nonetheless showy) flowering currants, together with their fruiting counterparts, the black, white and red currants and gooseberries, all of which (with the exception of blackcurrants) can be grown as cordons if space is a limiting factor. In areas where these fruits are grown on a large commercial scale (blackcurrants in particular), they can provide extensive bee forage areas.

The leaves are usually palmate and, together with the stems, often emit a distinct 'currant' odour, pleasant to some but not all. The individual flowers are small and somewhat tubular, but the numbers in each pendulous cluster are so large that when they are brightly coloured they make a considerable impact.

ORNAMENTAL TYPES

R. odoratum ⬥ ht: 6 ft *2 m* dist: 5 ft *1.5 m* Mar-Apr. Often sold as *aureum* which, if not botanically accurate, sounds more pleasant.

The odour in this case is a very pleasant one indeed, and if you have the space this golden-flowered currant is well worth having. The leaves are a shining green changing to gold in the autumn, and the black berries are particularly showy.

R. sanguineum ht: 9 ft *2.75 m* dist: 6-7 ft *2-2.25 m* Mar-Apr. The cultivars of this species are known as the flowering currants, and are available in a range of colours from white through the pinks to deep red. All have the distinctive musky currant smell. The black berries, unlike those of *odoratum* are not a very distinctive feature.

'Albescens' Flowers white with pink tinge.

'Brocklebankii' Golden-yellow leaves with pink flowers, rather less vigorous than the green-leaved forms.

'King Edward VII' Crimson flowers, rather less vigorous than the type.

'Pulborough Scarlet' Large deep-crimson flowers, well worth seeking out over and above any of the other listed cultivars.

R. speciosum (Fuchsia-flowered Currant) ht: 7-8 ft *2.25-2.5 m* dist: 6 ft *2 m* May. With its spiny stems and shiny leaves, this distinctive species is certainly not everyone's choice, but it is a superb sight when the branches are laden with rows of the short, pendulous, crimson flowers, from which protrude conspicuous red stamens. It comes into leaf in winter, long before it is sensible to do so, and as a consequence frequently suffers frost damage. Packing it in among other shrubs seems to give sufficient protection.

FRUITING TYPES ht: 4-5 ft *1.25-1.5 m* dist: 4-5 ft *1.25-1.5 m* Apr-May

These are all so well known as to make detailed descriptions unnecessary. Some recommended cultivars are listed below.

BLACKCURRANTS

'Blackdown' Fairly early flowering, resistant to mildew. 'Jet' Flowers later than most other cultivars, and therefore usually escapes frost damage. 'Ben Lomond' also flowers later and is resistant to mildew.

REDCURRANTS AND WHITECURRANTS

Protect the fruit of red and white currants against birds. Both may be grown as single or double cordons if space is limited, so buy them ready trained. Redcurrants are vigorous and will grow to 7-8 ft (2-2.5 m) if left unchecked. Recommended are; 'Red Lane', 'Stanza' (late flowering), and 'White Versailles'.

GOOSEBERRIES

These are unfortunately normally picked when immature — hard, green, flavourless bullets — then stewed into an even more flavourless pulp! After the bees have taken their fill of pollen and nectar from the flowers, leave the fruits to hang until August and September (true for most cultivars). You will know when they are really ripe by their colour and by giving them the 'squeeze test'. They may be well over 1½ in (3.5 cm) in diameter at this stage, and deliciously sweet and juicy. Cooking could only spoil them, in my opinion. Recommended are; 'Careless', pale greeny-white when ripe; 'Leveller', yellow when ripe; and 'Whinhams Industry', red when ripe.

Gooseberries may also be grown as cordons 12-18 in (30-45 cm) apart where space is limited.

As with all other fruit, correct and regular pruning is required if maximum crops are to be obtained.

* **Romneya coulteri** (Californian or Tree Poppy) Nec/Pol Shr. ht: 5-6 ft *1.5-2 m* dist: 3-4 ft *1-1.25 m* Jul-Oct, full sun

The six-petalled flowers, white and fragrant, can be up to 6 in (15 cm) in diameter and have as their centrepiece a large golden boss of stamens to which bees flock in great numbers. The overlapping petals have a satiny texture, and appear very flimsy in relation to their relatively large size, as they move easily in the slightest breeze.

The leaves are thick, 6 in (15 cm) or so long,

Romneya coulteri. The number of bees on this flower is evidence of its popularity.

glaucous and deeply cut, rather like a hand with the central 'finger' longest.

Romneya is classified as a shrub, although I always think of it as herbaceous, since the thick green stems are often killed back to the suckering rootstock in severe winters, from which new shoots are produced again in spring.

The fleshy rootstocks are sensitive to disturbance, so try to purchase pot-grown plants and thereafter move them only if it is really essential.

Any other species or cultivar would be just as suitable.

Rosa Pol. Shr. 🌱 ⚪
full sun

Everybody, or almost everybody, loves roses. If you doubt this, reflect on the fact that around 35 million are sold annually in Britain alone. With the average life of a rose at about ten years it will come as no surprise that nearly every garden in the country boasts at least a few plants. Why then are roses so popular? Well, the colour range, particularly of the smaller more commonly grown garden types, is truly enormous, with single colours, bi-colours, multi-colours, blends, stripes and the so-called hand-painted types. Add to this (in many cases) a delightful fragrance, long flowering season, with no long wait for the first flowers after planting, ease of culture, and you have the answer. Not perfect perhaps, but just what most of us require from a good garden plant. Many of the more commonly grown types — hybrid tea (now more correctly called 'large-flowered'), and to a lesser extent floribundas (now called 'cluster-flowered') — are largely unsuitable for the bee garden, since the flowers are mostly double or at best semi-double. For this reason hybrid tea roses will not be covered here.

The shrub roses are classified separately and they really are a mixture of old, nineteenth-century and new types. They are frequently taller and more robust than the types mentioned above, and often have a shorter flowering season. But, oh how they compensate for this with literally masses of flowers — single in many species and cultivars — which open to reveal a central boss packed with golden stamens. The fragrant flowers alone are attraction enough, but add to this a variety of other attributes (not all of which, it has to be said, can be found in any single plant) in the form of attractive foliage and fruit and even great 'winged' translucent red thorns, and you have one of the most versatile and beautiful of all plants. I certainly think of them as superior to many of the more 'exotic' and demanding shrubs that are often such a struggle to grow.

Climbers, and to a lesser extent ramblers, are also very popular, and the dwarf miniatures continue to increase in popularity. There are single-flowered species and cultivars of each of these types.

Do not forget to remove the old flowers when they are 'blown' and the stamens are brown. Failure to do so may well prevent more flowers from being produced. With only pollen on offer at a time of year when there is plenty else

Rose 'Eye Paint'. A spectacular cultivar.

available, roses will never be a beekeeper's first choice, but few will find this a reason for not growing at least some.

The selection here are among my favourites. If you see a rose you like that is not described here, then check its credentials in any good book on roses, and if it meets your requirements, buy it.

FLORIBUNDAS (Cluster-flowered) ◌ ⚘ Jun-Sep

Those cultivars with the fewest petals will obviously be your first choice — the singles and semi-doubles.

'Anna Wheatcroft' ht: 3 ft *1 m* dist: 18-24 in *45-60 cm* Large flat semi-double flowers of light vermilion. Slightly fragrant.

'Escapade' ht: 3 ft *1 m* dist: 18-24 in *45-60 cm* A most attractive rose with large flat blooms. The lilac petals are white towards the centre. Musk-like fragrance.

'Dainty Maid' ht: 3 ft *1 m* dist: 18-24 in *45-60 cm* Silvery pink petals with a carmine reverse, slightly fragrant.

'Eye Paint' ht: 5 ft *1.5 m* dist: 3-4 ft *1-1.25 m* Although the flowers are somewhat small, their colouring (scarlet with a white eye) and number more than compensate, and make this a real 'impact' plant.

'Fervid' ht: 3 ft *1 m* dist: 2 ft *60 cm* Vivid scarlet, slightly fragrant flowers that retain their colour well.

'Masquerade' ht: 3 ft *1 m* dist: 18-24 in *45-60 cm* This was the first multi-coloured cultivar to be produced. All the colour variations occur at the same time on the large flower trusses, yellow, pink and eventually dark red. It is free-flowering and slightly scented. Well worth a place in anyone's garden, beekeeper or not, and just as good in its diminutive form (Baby Masquerade) or its climbing form, described later.

'Paprika' ht: 2½ ft *75 cm* dist: 18 in *45 cm* The flowers are bright geranium red with a bluish tinge towards the base of the petals. Vigorous and easy to grow. The flowers do not suffer weather damage to the same degree as some other cultivars.

MINIATURES ⚘ Jun-Sep

As the name suggests, these roses are considerably smaller than either the hybrid teas or floribundas. Pretty enough, but I would not consider them worth growing except in the smallest garden, as an edging, and then only if I felt that I must have roses at any cost.

There are no single cultivars and few worthwhile semi-doubles.

'Josephine Wheatcroft' ht: 15 in *38 cm* dist: 12 in *30 cm* Bright yellow flowers.

'Perla De Montserrat' ht: 9 in *23 cm* dist: 6-9 in *15-23 cm* Clear pink flowers, paler at the edges.

'Starina' ht: 18 in *45 cm* dist: 12 in *30 cm* Orange-red flowers. Vigorous.

SHRUB ROSES ◌

The flowers and growth habits of these most diverse plants are as beautiful and varied as some of the group names would suggest — Musk, Bourbon, China, Gallica, Damask, Moss, Centifolia. You should not, however, be swayed by just a name. Make certain that the cultivar, species or variety you have seen in a garden, catalogue or book meets your requirements, particularly with regard to size (many of them are too large for the average garden and they do not respond well to the severe pruning meted out to hybrid teas and floribundas) and flowering period (flowering periods are frequently short). Single or semi-double flowers are also essential if the bees are to derive any benefit.

For reference purposes the group or type to which each rose belongs is shown in brackets after its name.

'Angelina' (Modern Shrub) ht: 3½ ft *105 cm* dist: 2½-3 ft *75-90 cm* Jul-Oct. Pretty deep-pink semi-double flowers with a white edge. Slightly fragrant.

'Ballerina' (Modern Shrub) ht: 4 ft *1.25 m* dist: 3 ft *1 m* Jul-Oct. Masses of single pink flowers with a large white edge are produced right through the summer and autumn. Slight musk fragrance. The small glossy leaves are attractive and complementary to the flowers.

'Berlin' (Modern Shrub) ht: 5 ft *1.5 m* dist: 4 ft *1.25 m* Jul-Oct. Large single orange-scarlet flowers produced intermittently over a long season. Slightly scented. Foliage dark and leathery, thorns large and red.

'Canary Bird' (Species) ht: 7 ft *2.25 m* dist: 5-6 ft *1.5-2 m* May-Jun. A very early and profuse flowerer, but it will not provide pollen for your bees for more than a few weeks. The flowers are bright yellow, single and about 2 in (5 cm) across. The foliage is grey-green and delicate with small leaflets.

'Frau Dagmar Hartopp' (Rugosa) ht: 5 ft *1.5 m* dist: 4 ft *1.25 m* Jul-Oct. Beautiful shell-pink flowers, 3½ in (9 cm) across, which are perfectly complemented by the dark Rugosa-type foliage. Superb large bright-red hips and good autumn leaf colour.

'Max Graf' (Rugosa) ht: 1 ft *30 cm* dist: 4 ft *1.25 m* Jul-Aug. Again the typical Rugosa foliage, carried on prostrate stems. Single pink fragrant flowers with a white centre. Unfortunately the flowering season is rather short. Good ground-cover plant.

'Nozomi' (Modern Shrub) ht: 2 ft *60 cm* dist: 4 ft *1.25 m* Jul-Aug. A neater but more sparse ground-cover plant than the preceding cultivar. The small pink flowers are carried in clusters and have no fragrance. Short flowering season. The foliage is dark green.

R. rubrifolia syn. *ferruginea* (Species) ht: 7 ft *2.25 m* dist: 5-6 ft *1.5-2 m* Jul-Aug. Flowers small, usually less than 2 in (5 cm) in diameter, pale pink with a white eye. Combined with handsome blue-grey foliage, this makes a fine plant for the mixed border. Bright red hips as early as August and September are a further bonus.

'Yesterday' ht: 3 ft *1 m* dist: 18-24 in *45-60 cm* Jul-Oct. Profuse, dainty, scented semi-double flowers, mauve-pink with a silver edge.

CLIMBERS Jun-Sep

Few private gardens now have the space or the budget for the traditional rose pergola. The best I have seen was on a good stiff Essex clay with a narrow grass path dividing the two long rows of numerous cultivars that grew along, up and over the rustic poles that made up the frame. Great clusters of deliciously fragrant flowers cascaded all around as you walked between them. A pleasant fantasy, but most gardens will only find space for one or two climbers, grown up a single pole, wigwam or on a wall.

'Altissimo' ht: 8 ft *2.5 m* Single 5 in (12.5 cm) blood-red slightly fragrant flowers that first appear in June.

'Dortmund' ht: 7 ft *2.25 m* Large single crimson flowers with a white edge, freely carried. No noticeable fragrance. Can, by severe pruning, be kept as a large 'shrub'.

'Masquerade' ht: 8 ft *2.5 m* The climbing form of the floribunda with its multi-coloured flower trusses. There can be few more spectacular sights than this rose in full flower viewed against a blue sky.

'Meg' ht: 12 ft *3.5 m* Salmon-apricot, semi-double flowers 5 in (12.5 cm) in diameter, with a large central boss of red-orange stamens. Fragrant.

* **Rosmarinus officinalis** (Rosemary) Nec/Pol Shr.
ht: 3-4 ft *1-1.25 m* dist: 2-3 ft *60-90 cm*
Apr-Jun, dry, salt tol, full sun
One of the constituents of the maquis, that glorious dense and strongly aromatic collection of plants found particularly in Corsica, but also in other Mediterranean regions. The hotter it becomes the stronger the aroma, but above all the distinctive aroma of rosemary can be distinguished. It is a veritable weed in these areas but is an important bee plant, and bees are invariably seen clustering on its pale blue flowers. The two-lipped flowers are grouped in the leaf axils along the branches on the previous season's growth.

123

The slender erect branches are thickly clothed with short, narrow unstalked leaves, glossy green above with inrolled margins partly obscuring the grey undersides.

Hard and long periods of frost may kill out parts of your plants and will almost certainly prevent them from reaching their full potential of 6 ft (2 m) in height. Rosemary is, however, a fast growing plant, so replacement should not be too much of a problem, especially if some cuttings are taken each year in August as an insurance against possible winter losses.

Only relatively hardy cultivars have been included here.

'Albus' White flowers.

'Majorca' Bright blue with a darker spot on the bottom flower lip.

'Miss Jessup's Variety' syn. 'Fastigiatus' A very erect form.

'Roseus' Lilac-pink flowers and somewhat less vigorous than the type.

'Severn Sea' Bright blue flowers, less upright with more arching branches.

* **Rubus** Nec/Pol Shr. ⚚ ⚘

Many of the plants in this genus are not only attractive to bees, they also bear edible fruits: blackberry, raspberry and loganberry (and the newer hybrids thereof). This group will be dealt with separately from the ornamental types, some of which are quite outstandingly decorative garden plants and attract bees in numbers commensurate with the large numbers of stamens.

BLACKBERRY or BRAMBLE Shr. ht: 10 ft *3 m* dist: 12-15 ft *3.5-4.5 m* Jul-Oct, full sun, semi-shade

This must be one of the most undisciplined of plants, with its long lax stems flopping in all directions and its tips rooting into the ground where they touch. It is, however, a major source of pollen and nectar (from the wild), when few others are available.

The blackberry's sprawling habit can only be tolerated if it is 'restrained' and trained in some way. If you have a post and wire fence then this will do reasonably well as a support — provided there is at least a clear 15 ft (4.5 m) run! Ideally, however, the support should be 6 ft (2 m) high with horizontal wires every foot (30 cm) for tying in. Train and tie all of one year's canes to one side and all the next year's to the other.

Dare I say that no-one in their right mind would grow the native blackberry in a garden setting — but there are good cultivars grown commercially both with and without thorns. The white or variably pink flowers are carried in clusters, and are an attractive feature.

The delicious shiny black fruits are too well known to need describing in detail and the leaflets, of which there are 5-7, are strongly serrated, dark green and similar in general appearance to those of the dog rose.

'Fantasia' Very large fruits. Both 'Oregon Thornless' (Thornless Evergreen) and 'Smooth-stem' are thornless, and may well appeal to the gardener who does not want to get bloodied when picking the fruit, a not infrequent occurrence with some of the older thorny cultivars such as 'Bedford Giant' and 'Himalayan Giant'.

RASPBERRY ht: 6-7 ft *2-2.25 m* dist: 12-18 in *30-45 cm* full sun, semi-shade

In areas where raspberries are widely grown (such as Tayside and Fife in northeast Scotland) the honey that is produced is highly prized and is regarded as perhaps the finest available. Bees are attracted in great numbers, even when dull conditions prevail, possibly because the sugar concentration in the nectar is very high. Flowering somewhat later than many other fruits the flowers, which are carried on short side shoots, are rarely damaged by frost; their pendulous habit also helps to prevent the nectar from being diluted by rain. As with oil seed rape, however, the honey granulates quickly and needs to be removed early.

The canes are usually supported by a post and wire fence, the numerous suckering shoots being tied in at a 3 in (7.5 cm) spacing.

'Malling Admiral' May-Jun. A good all-round cultivar with a long flowering and fruiting season.

Male catkins of Salix
caprea being mobbed
by honey bees.

'Malling Autumn Bliss' Jul-Oct. One of the newer and better autumn flowering/fruiting cultivars.

LOGANBERRY ht: 10 ft *3 m* dist: 12-15 ft *3.5-4.5 m* May-Jun, full sun

The fruits of the loganberry are a much darker red than those of the raspberry and also much longer. The clone LY654, usually simply called Thornless Loganberry, is widely available.

ORNAMENTAL TYPES

R. cockburnianus ht: 8 ft *2.5 m* dist: 5-6 ft *1.5-2 m* May-Jun, full sun, semi-shade

The gently arching thorny purple stems are heavily overlaid with a white bloom, making this a most striking plant during the long winter months. The leaves are grey-white, whilst the small but plentiful flowers are followed by black fruits.

R. x tridel 'Benenden' ht: 10 ft *3 m* dist: 8-10 ft *2.5-3 m* May-Jun, full sun. A most beautiful

and graceful shrub whose masses of pure white flowers, with their centres literally packed with golden stamens, are irresistible to bees. The flowers can be up to 3 in (7.5 cm) across and yield prodigious amounts of pollen. If you have the space, then this non-thorny cultivar is a must.

* **Salix** (Willow or Sallow) Nec/Pol
full sun, semi-shade

This is an enormously variable genus, including some giants, but also a good number of wild species (and perhaps an even larger number of hybrids arising from them). It is still well worth planting at least one species or cultivar in every garden, for they are a rich source of early pollen (the more showy male forms only), and it is wonderful to see the bees working the pollen-covered catkins in the early spring.

Both male and female plants yield nectar from yellowish glands at the base of the stamens or pistil, and these can clearly be seen if a large catkin of, say, *S. lanata*, is broken open. Try to make absolutely certain that the plants

125

you purchase are males, for as well as bearing no pollen the females flower far too early to be at all reliable as a nectar source.

Keep the larger tree willows well away from buildings and avoid the very tempting golden weeping willow (*S. x chrysocoma*), unless you have plenty of space and are prepared to spray it regularly for canker and scab: quite disfiguring diseases to which this hybrid is particularly susceptible. Spraying a small tree is easy, a large one is almost impossible.

Several of the willows, such as *alba* 'Britzensis' and *daphnoides*, are grown principally for their winter stem coloration, but for this to be retained they need to be cut down annually in spring. This means they look good over winter, but bear no catkins, so are of no use to our bees when so treated.

S. aegyptica Shr/T. ht: 18 ft *5.5 m* dist: 18 ft *5.5 m* Feb-Mar. Large bright yellow catkins and lance-shaped leaves carried on softly hairy grey twigs. Very showy.

S. caprea (Palm or Goat Willow) Shr/T. ht: 20-30 ft *6-9 m* dist: 20-30 ft *6-9 m* Feb-Mar. Usually seen as a large shrub or small tree and most conspicuous in the early spring when covered with the 1 in (2.5 cm) ovoid male catkins, rather like grey powder-puffs. These are crowded together at the ends of the branches and as the stamens emerge they turn a beautiful golden yellow. The female form is known as pussy willow and has longer, narrower grey catkins. A real favourite with bees and beekeepers alike, and if you have the space then the goat willow is a must.

'Pendula' T. ht: 7 ft *2.25 m* dist: 6-7 ft *2-2.25 m* Mar-Apr. This graceful weeping tree, very suitable for a small garden, is a delight, particularly during the winter and spring. As the leaves turn bright yellow and fall in the autumn, the small silver catkins protrude from the copper-coloured buds to provide bright silver dots down the trailing branches during the winter. In the spring the catkins increase in size, and at flowering time are the large fluffy yellow balls, covered in pollen, so beloved by the honey bee. This, of course, applies only to a male tree, which may be rather difficult to come by, but if you look around the garden centres in March the trees in containers should be in flower and a male can be selected.

S. hastata 'Wehrhanii' Shr. ht: 4 ft *1.25 m* dist: 4 ft *1.25 m* Feb-Mar. An ideal willow for the smaller garden. The reddish brown twigs are crowded with silvery white catkins which later turn yellow.

S. lanata (Woolly Willow) Shr. ht: 4 ft *1.25 m* dist: 4-5 ft *1.25-1.5 m* May-Jul. All too rare in most gardens, for it is a superb plant and in mid winter provides interest with its fat swollen woolly buds, persistent stipules and yellow stems. The male catkins are yellow and somewhat ovoid, up to 2 in (5 cm) long. Catkins of the female form may, however, lengthen considerably — up to 4 in (10 cm) — in fruit. The leaves are broad and handsome, almost circular, silvery grey and downy, turning a beautiful yellow in autumn.

Certainly a more interesting plant than *caprea* and an ideal substitute for it in the smaller garden.

S. melanostachys syn. *gracilistyla* Shr. ht: 6 ft *2 m* dist: 6 ft *2 m* May-Jun. This species has very distinctive catkins, the bud scales of which are black, opening to reveal brick-red anthers which turn yellow as they age. The grey-green leaves are 4 in (10 cm) in length.

S. reticulata Shr. ht: 6 in *15 cm* dist: 12-15 in *30-38 cm* May-Jun. Another rare willow, this time of diminutive form, which lives up to its name by having conspicuous net venation on its shiny roundish leaves. The erect catkins appear after the leaves. Well worth growing and ideal for the rock garden.

Many of the other willows will form very large plants indeed, so take great care before making a purchase, however attractive they appear. Two cultivars in this category very commonly seen in garden centres are the twisted-stem *matsudana* 'Tortuosa' (which anyway is only available in its female form), and *sachalinensis* 'Sekka', with its flattened and recurved stems.

None of the species listed needs a wet soil, and most are in fact very tolerant of dry conditions.

Salvia Nec/Pol
full sun
The scarlet salvias used for summer bedding schemes are not suitable for honey bees, since the two-lipped flower tube is far too long for them to reach the nectar. Fortunately there are many other salvias which do not have this disadvantage and are far more useful and decorative, and in some cases can be guaranteed to be covered in honey bees from the time the first flowers appear.

S. farinacea Ann. ht: 15 in *38 cm* dist: 12 in *30 cm* Jun-Nov. A fine annual bedding plant. The flower spikes bear masses of small violet-blue flowers encased in woolly white calyces. Far too decorative a plant to keep just for annual bedding schemes; use them also for herbaceous and shrub borders.

S. viridis syn. *horminum* (Clary) A(h). ht: 18 in *45 cm* dist: 6-9 in *15-23 cm* May-Oct. The small lilac-coloured flowers of this species are insignificant, hidden as they are by the large variously coloured bracts — pink, white, blue, and purple, with darker venation. The bracts retain their colour when dry and are very useful for winter decorations.

S. officinalis (Sage) Shr. ht: 2 ft *60 cm* dist: 2-3 ft *60-90 cm* May-Jul. A strongly aromatic shrub with thick grey-green wrinkled leaves and violet-blue flowers carried in loose whorls. The purple form 'Purpurescens' has darker flowers and the occasional variegated shoot, with splashes of pink, cream and purple. The golden sage 'Icterina' is particularly colourful, with its delightful marbled pale green, gold and lemon leaves. I have never seen it flower, but it may well do so in a drier, sunnier spot than where mine is located. I have all three forms in my garden and can never decide which one I like the best. They are all equally good for flavouring, and all three suffer in severe winters, for which reason I leave any pruning that is to be done until March so the tips of the shoots, even if they are dead, help to protect those lower down. Fortunately, cuttings taken any time between June and September root like weeds.
A dry soil is desirable but not essential.

S. x superba H. ht: 2 ft *60 cm* dist: 18 in *45 cm* Jun-Sep. Stiff spikes of intense purple-blue flowers with crimson bracts, set against grey-green leaves. The cultivar 'Lubeca' has deeper blue flowers, and both have persistent rusty brown dead flower heads and bracts, making an attractive end-of-season display.
Use these spikey plants in any border to help break up the mounded effect of the plant forms that dominate most gardens. Good bee and colour combinations would be *S. x superba* planted with grey foliage plants such as *Stachys lanata, Senecio* 'Sunshine' or *Salix lanata*.

Saxifraga (Rock Foil) Nec/Pol
Translated, Saxifraga literally means rock-breaker, an allusion to the effect that some of the species, particularly those that grow in rock crevices, will in time have on their 'homes'. The saxifrages are one of the darlings of the alpine plant enthusiasts, and justifiably so, for whether they form carpets or tight mounded hummocks there are few other alpines that flower so freely and in such a wide colour range. Unfortunately, the flowers are not especially popular with the bees, in spite of nectar being freely available. The flowers, with 4-5 rounded petals, are usually carried on branched stems which bear scale-like leaves. The true leaves can be very variable and in some species may be parsley-like, or toothed and paddle-shaped, or — showiest of all — linear and toothed with white encrustations of lime along their edges.
The choice is truly enormous, but I have limited it here to a few of my own particular favourites; try one or two and if, in spite of my predictions, your bees do make good use of them, plant some more!

S. x apiculata ht: 5 in *12.5 cm* dist: 9-12 in *23-30 cm* Mar-Apr, full sun, semi-shade. In spite of its name this easily grown hybrid is no more popular as a bee plant than any of the others listed. The clusters of small flowers are primrose yellow, with brighter yellow pollen. The leaves are linear, sharply pointed with the odd encrustation of lime along their edges. Hummock-forming.

S. x elizabethae ht: 5 in *12.5 cm* dist: 12 in *30*

127

Saxifraga apiculata, charming cushion-forming plants producing ample nectar in sunny conditions, but this is often shared with flies and other short-tongued insects.

cm Mar-Apr, full sun, semi-shade. Yellow flowers very freely produced on rapidly spreading mats of foliage. Planted with *x jenkinsae*, which has silvery foliage and pale pink flowers, there can be few more pleasing plant combinations. Plant both amongst rocks rather than 'on' them.

S. oppositifolia ≒ ht: 1 in *2.5 cm* dist: 9 in *23 cm* Mar-Apr, full sun. To my mind, the very best of all the saxifrages, with its bright pink ground-hugging flowers and bright orange-tipped stamens. The tiny rounded leaves are packed together and are completely obscured by the flowers. So striking is this plant when seen in a colourless windswept mountain setting it is difficult to believe that anything so beautiful and seemingly delicate could exist in such a place. Grows most happily in rock crevices throughout most of Europe.

S. paniculata syn. *aizoon* ⬭ ht: 9-12 in *23-30 cm* dist: 9-12 in *23-30 cm* May-Jun, full sun, semi-

shade. Forms dense tight hummocks of grey-green rosettes, a foot (30 cm) or so across. The rosettes are on short rooting stems, by which means it spreads itself.

The leaves can be up to 2 in (5 cm) long, slightly upturned at the ends, and with conspicuous saw-like teeth, all encrusted with limey deposits. The bases of all the leaves have conspicuous burgundy-red coloration.

The flower clusters are rather loose and the individual flowers rather small, usually white or pale cream in colour, although there are yellow and pink forms also. Very easily grown in rock crevices or in soil.

S. x urbium syn. *umbrosa* (London Pride) ≒ ht: 12 in *30 cm* dist: 8-9 in *20-23 cm* May-Jun, semi-shade. The cultivar 'Elliot's Variety', at 9-10 in (23-25 cm) is more dwarf than the type and carries masses of small star-like pink flowers.

'Mossy Saxifrages' ht: 4-9 in *10-23 cm* dist: 9-12 in *23-30 cm* Apr-May, semi-shade. The hybrid mossy saxifrages, so called because their mat-like foliage resembles moss, are perhaps the easiest to grow of all the saxifrages, and there are a large number of cultivars. 'Bob Hawkins' has variegated foliage and white flowers, whilst 'Red Admiral' has, as its name suggests, bright red flowers. All the cultivars are showy and well worth growing.

The majority of the saxifrages prefer limey soils and are best planted in rock gardens or scree beds in association with other alpines.

Scabiosa Nec/Pol H. ⚘
Jun-Oct, full sun

The wild blue scabious and its close relatives — visually and botanically — *Knautia* (Field Scabious) and *Succisa* (Devil's Bit Scabious), are found in abundance in hedgerows on dry banks, particularly on chalky soil, throughout most of Europe. All are equally attractive to bees and between them provide nectar from June to October. I have often thought of growing them in cultivation, since they are showy enough, but the availability of a quite wide range of larger-flowered garden types has prevented me — so far.

The outer florets of the flowers are generally much larger and appear like the petals of a normal flower. Each tubular-shaped floret has 4-5 lobes, is ¼ in (6 mm) or so long, and surrounded by dark brown sepals and a funnel-shaped structure with a 'grass skirt' attached to it, which partially covers the sepals. The long stamens protruding from the smaller inner florets earn the scabious one of its common names, the Pincushion Flower. All the scabious make good cut flowers.

S. atropurpurea (Sweet Scabious) ht: 2 ft *60 cm* dist: 9 in *23 cm* Comes in a range of colours from lilac to purple, the flowers being 2 in (5 cm) in diameter and fragrant. Although it is a short-lived perennial, *atropurpurea* is normally treated as a hardy annual.

S. caucasica ht: 3 ft *1 m* dist: 2 ft *60 cm* It is from this species that the best known garden cultivars have been derived, 'Bressingham White' and 'Clive Greaves' with flowers of a rich lavender blue with a paler centre. This last cultivar has deservedly been the most popular for many years. Newer dwarfer cultivars such as 'Butterfly Blue' will no doubt topple the old favourite in time.

'Moerheim Beauty' Deeper blue than 'Clive Greaves'.

S. graminifolia ht: 9 in *23 cm* dist: 6-9 in *15-23 cm* Flowers mauve-blue, with silvery foliage.

'Pinkushion' Pink flowers and silvery foliage.

Scilla Nec/Pol B/C.
full sun, semi-shade
Easily grown, showy, bulbous plants related to the hyacinths and grape hyacinths, mostly with blue nodding flowers that vary in shape from bell (as in the bluebell) to shallow dish (as in the vibrant *Scilla sibirica*). The flowers are in fact 'tepals', the petals and sepals being fused. The leaves are all basal, and long and narrow, sometimes barely appearing before the flowers.

Although they will not tolerate the dense shade beneath evergreens they do well enough beneath deciduous trees and close to deciduous shrubs, as long as it is not too dry. If they are happy you will soon know, for all the scillas seed themselves freely under such conditions.

Plant the bulbs about 2 in (5 cm) deep.

S. bifolia ht: 4 in *10 cm* dist: 4 in *10 cm* Mar-Apr. Flat star-shaped flowers, also available in white and pink forms.

S. non-scripta syn. *Endymion non-scriptus* syn. *Hyacinthoides non-scripta* ht: 12 in *30 cm* dist: 4-6 in *10-15 cm* Apr-Jun. The common bluebell is a vigorous plant that will soon smother plants of a less robust nature, so choose its companions with care. They are, of course, best located in a deciduous woodland setting where they look perfect and can colonize to their hearts' content. The small nodding flowers, of which there are several per stem, are truly bell-shaped and effectively prevent direct entry by the honey bee to the nectar. The six tepals are, however, divided to the base and it is not too difficult for the honey bee to gain access to the nectar via this route. At times when nectar is freely produced, it is also exuded between the tepals.

Pink and white forms are not uncommon in the wild, and are usually available commercially.

S. sibirica ht: 5 in *12.5 cm* dist: 3-4 in *7.5-10 cm* Mar-Apr. Deep gentian-blue, slightly cupped flowers, carried very freely, make this one of the most popular early spring-flowering bulbs. Ideal for the rock garden or naturalized in grass, it looks very well when planted in company with dwarf narcissus (such as 'Tête a Tête' or *bulbocodium*), or with primroses.

S. verna ht: 6 in *15 cm* dist: 4 in *10 cm* Mar-Jun. A pretty pale-blue-flowered plant, very suitable for the rock garden or naturalized in short grass. The flowers, which are relatively large — up to ⅔ in (16 mm) in diameter — are carried in terminal clusters of 2-12.

* Sedum Nec
full sun
There must be few gardens and even fewer gardeners and beekeepers who would want to manage without at least one of these easily grown plants. The individual flowers are small in size (similar to saxifrage) but large in number, literally hundreds of them being carried in flat heads in many of the species. The leaves are frequently large and with few

The common and tough stonecrop, Sedum acre, which grows abundantly on old stone walls, paths and any bare ground.

exceptions succulent, varying in shape from flat to cylindrical.

For convenience I have divided them into two groups; those suitable for rock gardens and those for herbaceous or even shrub borders.

ROCK GARDEN TYPES H. 🌿 ≢ dry

All the alpine-type species lend themselves well to hot dry situations such as paths, dry-stone walls and raised beds.

S. acre (Stonecrop) ht: 3 in *7.5 cm* dist: 12 in *30 cm* Jun-Jul. Many plants that are easy to grow tend to be despised and categorized as 'weeds', and it is certainly a fact that stonecrop is easy to grow and weed-like in its tendency to invade any piece of bare ground. The soil in my own garden is a rather light sandy loam and it positively revels in these conditions, filling any piece of bare ground (including gravel paths) that presents itself. It also managed to establish itself in a very much 'manicured' vegetable garden, and of course refuses to shrivel and die when pulled out and left on the surface like any normal weed should do! But for all that, it is one of my firm favourites, with its clusters of vibrant, yellow, star-like flowers, and the bees love it.

S. spathulifolium ht: 3 in *7.5 cm* dist: 12 in *30 cm* Jun-Jul. A compact plant that does spread but could not be described as invasive. The rosettes of spoon-shaped fleshy leaves are covered with a waxy grey bloom. The flower stems and older leaves are often bright red, and the yellow flowers are very similar to those of *acre*.

'Cappa Blanca' ht: 3 in *7.5 cm* dist: 12 in *30 cm* Jun-Jul. The leaf rosettes are silver-grey in winter, turning blue-grey in summer. Yellow flowers.

S. spurium 'Erdblut' ht: 6 in *15 cm* dist: 18 in *45 cm* Jun-Aug. Carmine flowers in dense heads.

'Schorbusser Blut' ht: 6 in *15 cm* dist: 18 in *45 cm* Jun-Aug. Red flowers.

HERBACEOUS OR SHRUB BORDER TYPES H. 🌲

S. maximum 'Atropurpureum' ht: 18 in *45 cm* dist: 18 in *45 cm* Aug-Sep. The thick fleshy leaves and stems are purplish-brown and provide interest from spring to autumn. The rose-pink flowers appear in the autumn and contrast well with the foliage.

S. rosea (Rose Root) ht: 12 in *30 cm* dist: 12 in *30 cm* May-Jun. The leaves are blue-grey and so closely packed that the stem supporting them is hidden. The lime-green flower heads are small and the leaves can be seen sticking out like a ruff when viewed from above. A striking plant for the spring garden.

S. spectabile ht: 18 in *45 cm* dist: 18 in *45 cm* Sep-Nov. There are many cultivars of this splendid, stiffly erect plant, with its great flat flower heads up to 8-9 in (20-23 cm) in diameter, which contain many hundreds of individual flowers. Most of the coloration comes from the four or five hollow inflated pistils, which look rather like a crown (as they do in most other *Sedum* species), and all types of bees and butterflies (peacock butterflies in my own garden) can frequently be seen, probing for nectar.

There are no petals as such. A quite beautiful flower when observed closely. The fleshy leaves are over 3 in (7.5 cm) long, grey-green and saw-

Sedum spectabile just coming into flower, with half a dozen bees already raiding its nectar.

toothed in the upper two thirds.

'Autumn Joy' ht: 2 ft *60 cm* dist: 2 ft *60 cm* Flowers rose-red at first, turning to russet in November.

'Brilliant' ht: 18 in *45 cm* dist: 18 in *45 cm* Bright rose-pink flowers.

'Meteor' ht: 18 in *45 cm* dist: 18 in *45 cm* Carmine-red flowers.

The fleshy stems, leaves and flowers of all *spectabile* cultivars dry to a beautiful russet-brown that makes it hard to despatch them to the compost heap, even when the new shoots are starting to grow in spring.

Sidalcea malvaeflora Nec/Pol H.
Jun-Aug, full sun, semi-shade
If you like hollyhocks but find them too tall for your garden, or you cannot grow them because of rust, that debilitating disease of hollyhocks, then the closely related sidalceas are an ex-cellent substitute, with their satiny pink, salmon or red flowers and large central boss of stamens smothered in pollen. Like the hollyhock, there is space and food enough for two or three bees to each flower. The flowers open progressively from the bottom of the 12-18 in (30-45 cm) flower spikes to give an extended flowering period.

The upper leaves are rather grass-like, with shallow lobes, whilst the lower ones are broader with larger lobes, rather like a rounded scabious leaf.

Sidalceas can also be raised from seed, now available from several seed companies.

'Croftway Red' ht: 3 ft *1 m* dist: 18-24 in *45-60 cm* The deepest red of all cultivars.

'Lovliness' ht: 2½ ft *75 cm* dist: 18 in *45 cm* Shell-pink flowers. A beautiful cultivar.

'Rose Queen' ht: 4 ft *1.25 m* dist: 3 ft *1 m* Clear rose-pink flowers.

'William Smith' ht: 3 ft *1 m* dist: 18-24 in *45-60 cm* Salmon-pink flowers.

131

Skimmia Nec/Pol Shr. 🌿 ⬭ ⚬ǀ⚬
ht: 3 ft *90 cm* dist: 2-3 ft *60-90 cm*
Mar-Apr, salt tol, semi-shade, shade
All species and cultivars of this slow-growing, delightfully neat evergreen are excellent early spring sources of nectar. Only some, however, produce pollen, for the plants are usually of separate sexes. The quantities of pollen carried in the small 4-5 petalled male flowers, carried in terminal clusters, are truly prodigious and provide a rich feast for the bees. If weather conditions are suitable, the female plants compensate aesthetically for their lack of pollen by bearing clusters of large, bright red, pea-sized berries, provided, of course, there is a male plant nearby. Odd berries may persist right through the winter, until the bushes come into flower again. The leaves are up to 4 in (10 cm) in length and emit a distinctive aroma when bruised, neither pleasant nor unpleasant. Unless otherwise stated, plant separate male and female plants if berries are required.

S. japonica A very variable species, probably due to the fact that it is often raised from seed. Can vary from 3-5 ft (1-1.5 m) in height.

'Foremanii' A very free-flowering form with large clusters of fruits.

'Fragrans' Like 'Rubella' this is an excellent pollinator and more free-flowering than any other species or cultivar, with the most wonderful fragrance imaginable from its greenish-white flowers.

'Rubella' The large clusters of bright red flower buds are carried right through the late autumn and winter and, unlike fruits, they are not taken by the birds. Providing pollen, nectar and winter colour, this must be one of the very best all-round garden and bee plants, and it will serve as a good pollinator for 'Foremanii'.

S. reevsiana syn. *fortunei* acid. There is no need for a pollinator for this slightly tender species. The fruits are a matt crimson-red, and are very persistent.

The elegant Sidalcea 'Rosea'.

Solidago (Golden Rod) Nec/Pol H. ⚐
Aug-Sep, full sun
Just about every garden in Britain used to have one of these tough, easily grown plants. The plume-like inflorescences are made up of small yellow flowers, held well above the leaves. These original types are not often seen in gardens now, since there are many newer, more compact and floriferous cultivars available, but they have naturalized themselves quite happily on waste ground and by the side of railway tracks, where they are eagerly sought out by honey bees.

The bulk of the species are from North America, where they are regarded as important bee plants, but *Solidago virgaurea* is widely distributed in Britain and Europe. It is of particular use to the bees since it has a very long flowering season — June to September — but has little merit as a garden plant.

The leaves of all species are rather narrow, almost lance-shaped.

'Cloth of Gold' ht: 18 in *45 cm* dist: 1 ft *30 cm*
Deep yellow flowers.

'Golden Shower' ht: 2½ ft *75 cm* dist: 2 ft *60 cm*
The deep yellow flower plumes of this cultivar are more arching and informal than many others.

'Golden Thumb' ht: 12 in *30 cm* dist: 9 in *23 cm*
The leaves of this robust little plant take on some of the deep yellow flower coloration.

Sorbus Nec/Pol T. ⚐ ⚬ǀ⚬
May-Jun, salt tol, full sun
A marvellously decorative genus of trees and shrubs with so many attributes that every garden should have one, and since there are species that grow to no more than 18 in (45 cm) high there can be no excuse! They are all absolutely hardy, growing in the most exposed sites, and many are salt-spray resistant. The leaves are toothed and may be simple in shape, as in the *aria* (whitebeam) group, or much divided, rather like the dog rose, in the *aucuparia* (rowan or mountain ash) types. In many species and cultivars the autumn leaf colour can be quite breathtaking, with yellows, reds, coppers and combinations of all three

133

The rowan, Sorbus aucuparia, has the advantage of good autumn foliage and bright red berries, as well as being a 'bee plant'.

colours on the same plant. Add to this the brilliant clusters of red, red-purple, white, pink, or yellow berries and you have a warming sight for the coldest of autumn days. The masses of flat-headed clusters of small white flowers are not unattractive and are worked with some enthusiasm (especially the white-beam) by honey bees.

For some unknown reason the birds (which can strip a tree in the space of two or three hours) seem to prefer red and orange berries to yellow or white, and it is not uncommon to see white-berried species, such as *hupehensis* un-touched in late January — an added bonus, but one the beekeeper may not worry too much about.

S. aria (Whitebeam) ☁ ht: 40 ft *12 m* A beautifully proportioned tree with oval leaves up to 4½ in (11.5 cm) long, the upper surfaces grey at first, turning green as they mature, intensely grey-white beneath. Good russet-gold autumn colour, deep crimson berries. Rather too large for the average sized garden. The cultivar 'Lutescens' is more widely grown and has the upper leaf surfaces covered in dense creamy white hairs, turning grey in autumn.

AUCUPARIA TYPES (Dog-rose leaves)

'Beissneri' ⚚ ht: 30 ft *9 m* An erect cultivar

with beautiful, shiny copper-russet bark, which literally glows in even the weakest winter sunshine. The leaves are deeply toothed, almost 'ferny' and pale green, especially when young, whilst the leaf stalks and stems of young shoots are a dull red. You may have difficulty in finding this cultivar in the average garden centre, but it is well worth seeking out.

'Fastigiata' ht: 15 ft *4.5 m* An erect slow-growing tree with a compact growth habit and large bright red fruits.

'Xanthocarpa' syn. 'Fructuluteo' ☁ ht: 30 ft *9 m*. A cultivar with amber-yellow fruits.

S. cashmeriana ☁ ht: 15 ft *4.5 m* The white flowers, flushed with pink, of this small graceful tree or large shrub are worked with great enthusiasm by bees. The elegant leaves have 17-19 strongly serrated leaflets and colour well in autumn. The glistening white drooping fruits are almost ½ in (1.3 cm) in diameter and hang on until well after the leaves have fallen.

S. hupehensis ⚚ ht: 20 ft *6 m* This species has white berries with a pink tinge. The branches are a distinct purplish-brown, whilst the leaves have a bluish-green cast with good red autumn coloration.

'Joseph Rock' An outstanding cultivar with

134

creamy-yellow fruits, but it is so susceptible to fireblight (see section on *Cotoneaster*) that it is probably not worth the risk of trying it in southern Britain or Europe, where the disease has reached epidemic proportions due to the milder climate.

S. reducta ⬡ ht: 18 in *45 cm* A dwarf suckering shrub, ideal for the rock or peat garden. The petioles are red and the leaflets shiny, turning reddish-purple to bronze in autumn. The small fruits are white flushed with pink.

S. sargentiana ⚘ ht: 30 ft *9 m* A superb species with leaves up to 1 ft (30 cm) in length, and large sticky buds, rather like those of the horse-chestnut, but bright red in colour. The scarlet autumn leaf colour is outstanding. The fruits are small but the clusters can be up to 6 in (15 cm) across.

S. vilmorinii ⬡ ht: 12 ft *3.5 m* An elegant, wide-spreading small tree or shrub. The dark green fern-like leaflets, which number up to 31, turn a reddish-purple in autumn. The loose clusters of berries are dark red at first, turning to pink and then white with a pink flush.

Stachys (Woundwort) Nec/Pol
full sun

A handsome and distinctive genus of plants, of which there are several species native to Britain and Europe. Two of these, *S. sylvatica* (Wood Woundwort) and *S. germanica* (Downy Woundwort) are worth growing in their own right.

The upright square-stemmed flower spikes that are so typical of Labiatae bear whorls of distinctly two-lipped flowers. The narrow flower tubes rarely exceed ¼ in (6 mm) and thus allow easy bee access. All species thrive on poor dry soils.

S. byzantina syn. *lanata* (Lambs' Ears) H. ⬡ ⚘ ht: 9 in *23 cm* Jul-Sep. One of the best and most easily grown of all ground-cover plants, with surely one of the most appropriate common names. The narrowly elliptic leaves generally persist through the winter and are covered on both surfaces with perhaps the most dense woolly hair of any plant. They are irresistible to the touch and feel softer than down. The pale

lavender flowers that peep through the woolly calyces look absolutely right. No wonder Gertrude Jekyll used this marvellous plant so freely.

The cultivar 'Silver Carpet', which looks very similar, rarely flowers, so if you are uncertain of the identity of a plant, check for flower spikes in August before purchasing.

S. grandiflora syn. *Betonica macrantha* (Betony) H. ⚘ ht: 18 in *45 cm* May-Jun. A distinctly different plant to *byzantina*, with no hair present on leaves or stems. The leaves are up to 3 in (7.5 cm) long, ovate with nicely scalloped edges, and also deeply veined. Flowers purple. The cultivar 'Rosea' has pink flowers.

* Stranvaesia Nec/Pol Shr. ⬡ ⚘ ⚘
Jun-Jul, full sun, semi-shade

A handsome vigorous evergreen, rather similar to the cotoneasters and, like them, very susceptible to fireblight. The leaves are lance-like and leathery, up to 5 in (12.5 cm) long. The leaf stalks and new buds are a very attractive burgundy-red, particularly during the winter months, and as the leaves are quite close together this is a very distinctive feature. Some of the leaves also take on a red coloration, particularly during cold weather, and this adds to the winter display.

The creamy-white flowers are carried profusely in loose clusters on short side shoots and are followed by crimson fruits fully ⅓ in (8 mm) across, which hang late in to the winter since birds do not seem to favour them as food. The flowers are extremely attractive to all bees and will be covered in bumble and honey bees collecting both nectar and pollen.

S. davidiana ht: 15 ft *4.5 m* dist: 8-10 ft *2.5-3 m* The flowers are white but have red anthers. You may see *salicifolia* offered in garden centres, and there is little difference between this and *davidiana*, both producing some very stiffly erect branches.

S. undulata ht: 8 ft *2.5 m* dist: 6-8 ft *2-2.5 m* Rather more spreading in habit, often growing wider than it does high. The leaves are usually wavy at the margins.

Symphoricarpos (Snowberry) Nec/Pol Shr. ⅄ ⦿⬥⬥
full sun, shade

This is a 'grow anywhere' shrub with a most invasive suckering habit. Left unchecked a single plant will in about ten years cover 50 yds (45 m) or so of ground. However, if it is kept under control regularly, and by this I mean twice a year, by removing suckers and spreading branches, it is a most rewarding shrub. The rounded leaves are carried on slender twiggy shoots that are so much a characteristic of this genus, mid green above, pale beneath.

The tiny bell-shaped flowers are carried in dense terminal clusters, and are much sought after by honey bees. The five petals are pink on the outside and white inside, where they are also distinctly hairy. The round berries that follow are marble size, pink or white and pleasantly squidgey — rather like hard-boiled eggs without their shells. These are carried well into the winter, as the birds do not like them.

S. albus (Snowberry) ⬭ ht: 6 ft *2 m* dist: 6-8 ft *2-2.5 m* This is the North American plant that most of us know. It has naturalized itself happily more or less throughout Europe in hedgerows and waste places, and you must be vigilant, as I have already said, if you do not want it to take over. I have two large specimens and curse them on occasion, but they are unlikely to ever be dug out.

S. x chenaultii 'Hancock' ≡ ht: 3 ft *1 m* dist: 4 ft *1.25 m* The absolute maze of prostrate stems that this hybrid builds up never ceases to amaze me, with a capacity to smother out any weed seeds that are unlucky enough to find themselves beneath its branches. The berries are purple to white. The other hybrids and cultivars tend not to produce suckers, so are less invasive.

S. x doorenbosii 'Magic Berry' ⬭ ht: 3 ft *1 m* dist: 4 ft *1.25 m* Rose-pink berries very freely produced.

'Mother of Pearl' ht: 3 ft *1 m* dist: 4 ft *1.25 m* Pink berries.

'White Hedge' ht: 4 ft *1.25 m* dist: 4-5 ft *1.25-1.5 m* White berries carried freely.

Syringa (Lilac) Nec/Pol Shr. ⅄ ⬭
full sun, semi-shade

The glorious fragrance of the dense flower clusters of lilac in the May garden is unmistakable. In many, but not all species the tubes of the four-petalled flowers are too long for the honey bee to gain access to the nectar. But, being narrow, nectar 'flooding' can quickly take place in sunny weather, thus allowing partial access at least. The flowers of many of the cultivars grown are double and must constitute the ultimate frustration for bees: nectar out of reach and no pollen! Choose only those forms with single flowers and short tubes, if you want the best of both worlds. Also, consider carefully if you are prepared to give 'house room' to what are mostly quite large plants with relatively short flowering periods, with little else to offer, the leaves producing little in the way of summer attraction or autumn colour.

Flowering at the same time as many rhododendrons, and with a similar colour range, lilacs should be grown in their stead if the soil is alkaline, for they will thrive as very few other plants can at a high pH.

To ensure a good display in successive years, cut off the old flower spikes as soon as they fade.

S. microphylla 'Superba' ht: 6 ft *2 m* dist: 4 ft *1.25 m* Apr-May and Aug. With its small oval leaves and slender branches this is not at all a typical lilac. The rosy-lilac flower clusters are relatively small and erect, and with its longer-than-average flowering season and neat habit this is an excellent bee and garden plant.

S. velutina syn. *palabiniana* ht: 4 ft *1.25 m* dist: 4 ft *1.25 m* May-Jun. The velvety dark-green leaves of this dwarf species are quite distinct, and beautifully complement the pale lavender-pink flowers.

S. x prestoniae ht: 12 ft *3.5 m* dist: 12 ft *3.5 m* May-Jun. The individual flowers of this vigorous hybrid are small but are carried in their thousands. There is a range of cultivars available, all of which have predominantly darkish-pink to burgundy-red flowers.

A magnificent plant if you have the space, the purple buds providing their own display during May, before the flowers open.

S. vulgaris ht: 10 ft *3 m* dist: 8 ft *2.5 m* May-Jun. This is the familiar common lilac, parent of so many of the garden cultivars and hybrids. Those listed all have single flowers.

'Marachel Foch' Bright carmine-rose flowers.

'Maud Notcutt' Very large white flowers.

'Primrose' Yellow flowers.

'Souvenir de Louis Spaeth' Deep wine-red flowers.

Thymus (Thyme) Nec. Shr. 🌿
dry, full sun

A wonderful genus of dwarf erect or carpeting herbs or shrubs, with strongly aromatic foliage and pink or mauve flowers. The prostrate types are ideal for 'gaps' in paved areas or rock-garden paths, where they yield up their spicy aroma with each step taken. They are also ideal 'cascade' plants for walls and rocks. They will, however, need to be taken in hand when grown in company with other alpines, for they are invasive and will surround and swamp any of their weaker companions.

The individual flowers are tiny, less than ¼ in (6 mm), and distinctly two-lipped, the upper notched, the lower divided into three. The flowers open progressively from the base of the rounded heads or spikes. In just one such ⅓ in (8 mm) head, I have counted 38 individual flowers, and on the species in question, *T. leucotrichus*, the flower heads are so close that there are no leaves in sight at all. There must, therefore, be around 50,000 flowers during the season for my bees, in just one square foot of plant!

The thymes are certainly excellent bee plants and are widely distributed in the wild, especially in the southern parts of Europe where considerable crops of thyme honey are taken — some, such as Mount Hymettus honey, being world famous. The three species commonly found wild in Britain are also happiest in the south, since they all really prefer dryish conditions. Many of the excellent golden and silver foliage types do not flower freely enough to warrant mention here.

T. serpyllum syn. *praecox arcticus* ⇌ ht: 3 in *7.5 cm* This species includes most of the more commonly grown thymes.

'Albus' dist: 3-4 ft *1-1.25 m* Jun-Aug. Deep green foliage with white flowers. Rampant.

'Coccineus Major' dist: 2 ft *60 cm* Jun-Aug. Dark foliage and crimson flowers.

'Doone Valley' dist: 9 in *23 cm* Jul-Oct. A beautiful cultivar with dark green leaves irregularly splotched with gold. The pale lavender flower heads are its crowning glory, and there can be no finer colour combination of leaves and flowers in the whole plant kingdom.

'Pink Chintz' dist: 2 ft *60 cm* Jun-Aug. Salmon-pink flowers.

T. languinosus ⇌ ht: 4 in *10 cm* dist: 3 ft *1 m* Jun-Aug. Grey-green leaves with long hairs, particularly at the edges. Vigorous.

T. leucotrichus ⟨⟩ ht: 9 in *23 cm* dist: 1 ft *30 cm* May-Aug. Dark grey-green leaves and pink flowers in profusion, before any other species is even showing bud colour.

T. necifferi ⇌ ht: 3 in *7.5 cm* dist: 18 in *45 cm* Jun-Aug. Narrow grey hairy leaves and pink flowers carried on long trailing shoots. Quite different from the other species.

Tilia (Lime or Linden) Nec/Pol T. 🌱
full sun, semi-shade

With the demise of the elm in western Europe the lime is once more in the ascendancy as an avenue, hedge and general park and estate tree. This is good news for the beekeeper, for the lime is a most important source of nectar in some areas of Britain, for example around Birmingham and London, but in most other areas of Britain little nectar is obtained from these trees. The sweetly fragrant flowers are in pendant clusters, and the flower stalks are attached to the 2-3 in (5-7.5 cm) pale-green bracts which are such a distinctive feature of all limes. Lime honey has a very pleasant slightly minty flavour and a greenish tinge to its colour. A small quantity of pollen is obtained, but bees seem to have trouble in collecting it.

Like some other trees, limes carry a host of

aphids during the summer, and these secrete quantities of sticky honeydew over the leaves. This is used as food by the aptly named sooty mould, which can often be seen covering the leaves with black smudges in late summer. Honeydew is also collected by the honey bee, yielding a honey which can vary from golden to almost black in colour, with a rich flavour particularly reminiscent of dried figs in the darker samples. Some honeydew honeys are much prized, the best known being Black Forest Pine honey, which is produced from the exudation of the pine aphids.

The nectar of some lime species, particularly *petiolaris, x euchlora, tomentosa* and *orbicularis*, can at times stupefy and even kill bees, and it has been suggested by those who have access to large collections of different species of lime that to a certain extent all have some degree of toxicity. The toxicity seems to vary from year to year, and to affect bumble bees with greater severity than honey bees.

If you have a large garden and the patience to wait 12-15 years for the first flowers, then you might like to try one of the less vigorous species listed.

T. miqueliana ⬡ ht: 20-30 ft *6-9 m* Aug. A slow-growing, late-flowering species. The broad and slightly lobed leaves are carried well into the autumn.

T. platyphyllos 'Laciniata' ⚶ ht: 15-20 ft *4.5-6 m* Jul. Leaves deeply serrated.

Tradescantia (Spiderworts) Nec/Pol H. ⚶
ht: 2 ft *60 cm* dist: 18 in *45 cm* Jun-Oct, full sun, semi-shade

Erect herbaceous plants with many long narrow leaves sticking out in all directions, often almost at right angles to the stem. The rather flat three-petalled flowers are carried in terminal clusters and may be up to 2 in (5 cm) across, in a wide range of colours. The stamens are attractively bearded and the six anthers are a quite bright yellow.

The flowering period is long in any reasonable soil, and they are firm favourites in my own garden. All the following are cultivars of *x andersonii* (previously *virginiana*).

'Isis' Oxford blue flowers.

'Osprey' The flowers are pure white with a pale-lavender 'beard'.

'Purewell Giant' Bright carmine flowers.

'Purple Dome' Deep violet-blue flowers.

Tricyrtis Nec. H. ⚶
Sep-Oct, full sun, semi-shade

Toad Lily is not the most alluring name for a plant with such pretty flowers. The plant takes this name from the three swollen nectaries at the base of the flowers, which are carried singly or in groups, and are variously and distinctly spotted according to species. The six pointed tepals are fused at the base, but then flare out so that each can be seen quite separately. For the rest, the flowers are similar to those of the lilies. The root system is rhizomatous and does not always survive cold winters; some dry peat or leaves spread over the plants in November will afford a degree of protection.

Good drainage, coupled with a soil sufficiently high in organic matter to retain moisture, is essential for success.

T. formosana ht: 2 ft *60 cm* dist: 18 in *45 cm* The erect flowers are pale purple with darker spots and a yellow throat. Leaves up to 5 in (12.5 cm) long.

T. hirta ht: 2 ft *60 cm* dist: 2½ ft *75 cm* Flowers erect, held close to the stem, either solitary or in groups, white with purple spots. The white form 'Alba' is usually more dwarf.

Tulipa (Tulips) Pol. B/C. ⚶
full sun

The tulips are so well known as to require very little in the way of a detailed description. They range from the garish, doubles and parrots, through the elegant, lily-flowered, to the dwarfer, more interesting and generally less vulgar species and their cultivars. These latter seem to be growing in popularity — an interesting backlash to the excesses of the plant breeders, and long may it continue.

The English national collection of tulip species is held at the University Botanic

Garden, Cambridge, and is well worth a visit in spring. Unlike the more 'fancy' cultivars, the species and their cultivars could well do with a popularity boost, which I will here attempt to give them. All look best when closely planted in groups, although they may be used in conjunction with dwarf spring bedding plants such as *Arabis, Bellis* or pansy.

Although tulips produce a mass of pollen, mostly yellow, they are not front-rank bee plants since they are not sought out when other more palatable sources are available. They do not, however, take up much space and may be a welcome change from the more normal yellow and blue spring bulb colours.

Plant the bulbs 4-6 in (10-15 cm) deep in rock gardens or at the edge of shrub or herbaceous borders, where they will be able to dry out thoroughly during the summer. This 'baking' always seems to result in a better display of flowers the following spring.

T. clusiana (Lady Tulip) ht: 8 in *20 cm* dist: 4-6 in *10-15 cm* Apr. The outside of the petals is rose-red, the interior creamy-white, with a purple base. The leaves may be red-edged.

T. eichleri ht: 10 in *25 cm* dist: 4-6 in *10-15 cm* Apr. Scarlet petals with a shiny black base, margined with yellow.

T. fosteriana ht: 12 in *30 cm* dist: 4-6 in *10-15 cm* Apr. Large scarlet flowers with a black basal blotch, margined with yellow within. Several cultivars are available.

T. greigii ht: 8 in *20 cm* dist: 4-6 in *10-15 cm* May. There is a very wide range of these slightly later-flowering striped and marble-leaved cultivars. Some, such as 'Cape Cod' can be 18 in (45 cm) or so in height, but most of them average 8-10 in (20-25 cm).

T. kaufmanniana (Water-lily Tulips) ht: 5-9 in *12.5-23 cm* dist: 4-6 in *10-15 cm* Mar. In common with other species, the bulbs of *kaufmanniana* do not need to be lifted annually, but unlike many of these other species, which tend to weaken in time, *kaufmanniana* proliferates and gets stronger each year. The number of cultivars is legion and most of them have their large leaves attractively splotched and marbled with dull purple.

T. praestans 'Fusilier' ht: 10 in *25 cm* dist: 4-6 in *10-15 cm* Apr. One to six orange-scarlet flowers are produced on each stem of this very showy cultivar. I grow it in a narrow sunny border with pink *Helianthemums*, the first flowers of which start to appear in late April, just as those of the tulip have passed their best.

T. humilis syn. *pulchella* ht: 4 in *10 cm* dist: 4 in *10 cm* Mar. A red dwarf with flowers which may vary in colour from very pale pink to crimson and even dull red-purple. The blotch at the base of the petals may be yellow or black.

T. tarda ht: 5 in *12.5 cm* dist: 4 in *10 cm* Apr. There are 3-6 white star-shaped flowers with a broad variable green stripe, edged with yellow, on the exterior. The whole of the centre of the flower is yellow, producing rather a 'fried egg' effect. A very pretty flower indeed.

Ulex (Gorse, Furze or Whin) Nec/Pol Shr. 🐝
dry, salt tol, full sun
Before you dismiss this somewhat antisocial plant that grows wild anyway, pause — for there is a dwarf form, and the gorse has many attributes, one of which (its ability to produce some flowers every day of the year) is very rare. The musky flower scent is also quite addictive, particularly when the bushes are in full flower, covered with showers of the chrome-yellow pea-like flowers. Gorse thrives on the very poorest of soils (as evidenced by its frequent presence on heathland areas), and needs no pruning, fertilizers or fuss. It may not be everyone's choice, but it is quite a popular bee plant and does produce enormous amounts of pollen.

In common with most other legumes gorse does not like root disturbance, so buy a pot-grown plant or collect some of the black-brown pods and sow their seeds in situ; they are easily raised from seed.

U. europaeus ht: 6 ft *2 m* dist: 4-6 ft *1.25-2 m* Mar-May. The common gorse of British heathlands.

U. minor ht: 2 ft *60 cm* dist: 2 ft *60 cm* Jul-Oct. Autumn flowering, with paler yellow small flowers.

Verbascum (Mullein) Nec/Pol H. ⚘
Jun-Aug, full sun

From a basal rosette of ovate to lance-shaped leaves, which in many species are covered with soft hairs, the mulleins produce their stiffly erect single or branched flower spikes. These will persist for years if not cut down after flowering, particularly in a hot dry climate, where they are often a distinctive feature of the landscape. A second flush of flower spikes — somewhat shorter — will often be produced in September, October or even November if the old spikes are cut back as soon as they finish flowering. The flower spikes are packed with the shallowly cupped flowers (similar to *Potentilla*) about 1½ in (3.5 cm) in diameter, each with five lobes; the 'bottom' lobe is central and is larger than the other four. The five stamens are densely covered with soft white hairs, giving the flower centre a very woolly appearance, and from this 'wool' the bright orange anthers peep. The single stigma seems to push through at any angle where there is a gap in the hairs. The bases of the petals are also hairy.

Few of the verbascums are long-lived, and replacement within two years may prove necessary. They do tend to seed themselves reasonably freely, so these seedlings could act as the replacements, but some variation in shape, size and colour should be expected. Taking cuttings of basal shoots that have not flowered is another alternative and these new plants will, of course, be exactly the same as the parents.

Good drainage is essential, and it does not really seem to matter how dry the soil. Several species are found growing in the wild in Britain, particularly in the south and southeast on calcareous soils, and even more species in southern Europe, particularly the Mediterranean regions.

V. bombyciferum ht: 5 ft *1.5 m* dist: 2-3 ft *60-90 cm*
A handsome plant, covered with a dense felt of silver hair, and with leaves over 1 ft (30 cm) long. The flowers are bright yellow. 'Silver Spire', is paler than the type and available from some seedsmen, and is not a difficult plant to raise.

V. chaixii syn. *vernale* ht: 3 ft *1 m* dist: 18 in *45 cm*
Yellow flowers with purple stamens.

V. dumulosum ht: 12 in *30 cm* dist: 12 in *30 cm*
White felted leaves, and yellow flowers with purple stamens. Needs a sheltered spot or some other form of winter protection.

V. x 'Letitia' ht: 9 in *23 cm* dist: 9 in *23 cm* Masses of bright yellow flowers, leaves covered with silvery hairs.

V. phoenicum ht: 4 ft *1.25 m* dist: 2 ft *60 cm* Many of the cultivars and hybrids in cultivation are derived from this species.

'Bridal Bouquet' White flowers blushed with pink.

'Cotswold Queen' Buff flowers.

'Gainsborough' Flowers a bright canary yellow.

'Hartley' Multi-coloured flowers of buff and plum-purple.

'Pink Domino' Darker leaved and slightly shorter than the cultivars listed above, with rose-pink flowers.

Veronica (Speedwell) Nec/Pol H.
full sun, semi-shade

All the speedwells have short or long flower spikes and a very long flowering season, making them both elegant and desirable as garden plants, eagerly sought out by honey bees whenever and wherever they are in flower. The individual flowers have four or five widely spreading lobes, each conspicuously veined in a darker shade of the ground colour. The flower tube is short and a ring of hairs in the pale eye protects the nectar at the base of the ovary. The two stamens stick out from the petticoat — like flowers with two legs, with the anthers as feet.

Tall and dwarf species have been separated in the text below.

TALL SPECIES ⚘

With their long elegant flower spikes these all contrast well with plants of rounded form.

V. gentianoides ht: 2 ft *60 cm* dist: 18 in *45 cm* May-Jun. This has spikes of pale blue flowers, 10 in

(25 cm) long, ½ in (1.3 cm) or so across, and broadly oblong leaves. The variegated form has an irregular white edging to the leaves, and is a first-class plant, slightly less vigorous than the type.

V. longifolia 'Foersters Blue' ht: 2 ft *60 cm* dist: 18 in *45 cm* Jul-Sep. Deep-blue flowers.

V. spicata ht: 18 in *45 cm* dist: 1 ft *30 cm* Jun-Jul. Spikey blue flowers.

'Blue Fox' Deep blue flowers.

'Red Fox' Crimson flowers.

V. s. incana Silvery foliage with deep-blue flowers, variable when raised from seed.

V. teucrium 'Crater Lake Blue' ht: 1 ft *30 cm* dist: 9 in *23 cm* Jul-Sep. A superb plant with dense spikes of deep-blue flowers.

V. virginica ht: 4 ft *1.25 m* dist: 3 ft *1 m* Aug-Oct. Long, elegant flower spikes of very pale blue. The form 'Alba' has white flowers.

DWARF SPECIES 〒

Very easily grown plants, ideal for the rock garden, scree or border, spreading quickly to give excellent ground cover.

V. prostrata 'Blue Sheen' ht: 9 in *23 cm* dist: 1 ft *30 cm* May-Jun. Powder-blue flowers.

'Trehane' Golden leaves and deep-blue flowers.

V. spicata incana 'Nana' ht: 9 in *23 cm* dist: 1 ft *30 cm* Jul-Sep. A dwarf version of *spicata incana* (see above).

The almost irresistible germander speedwell (*V. chamaedrys*) should be admired in the wild, for it is the very devil to get rid of once it has established itself in a lawn or border. It is certainly a lovely sight, with its deep-blue flowers in early March, and I am very happy to see them on the wilder fringes of my garden.

* **Viburnum** Nec/Pol Shr.
full sun
A very hardy and easily grown genus of plants containing a large number of species and cultivars, amongst which are some of the best of all garden shrubs. The small, five-petalled tubular flowers, which make up the often flat or rounded flower heads, are in many cases deliciously fragrant and may be followed by showy fruits.

The evergreen viburnums generally have large heavily veined leaves, whilst the deciduous species in many cases give good autumn colour effects.

Nectar production can be very variable, especially on the winter-flowering species.

V. x bodnantense 'Dawn' ht: 10 ft *3 m* dist: 8-10 ft *2.5-3 m* Nov-Mar. Clusters of fragrant deep pink flower buds, opening to paler pink before any leaves appear, make this one of the best winter-flowering shrubs.

V. carlesii ht: 4 ft *1.25 m* dist: 4 ft *1.25 m* Apr-May. A deservedly popular shrub with pale green leaves that colour well in autumn, and clusters of pink sweetly fragrant flowers. These open to white, and are followed by small black fruits. The cultivar 'Aurora' is redder in bud and opens to pink, with the same delicious fragrance.

V. davidii ht: 3 ft *1 m* dist: 4 ft *1.25 m* May-Jun, salt tol. A marvellous ground-cover plant with deep-green, heavily veined elliptical leaves which may be up to 6 in (15 cm) in length. The leaf stalks (particularly in winter) turn dull burgundy red, as do the flower buds that sit waiting all winter long for warm early summer weather before they open. The flowers are white and dainty.

The female plants, which you will not particularly want, occasionally bear small turquoise fruits which contrast beautifully with the dark green foliage. Few garden centres label their plants male and female, so you will either have to take pot luck or inspect the plants in flower.

V. farreri syn. *fragrans* ht: 8 ft *2.5 m* dist: 6-8 ft *2-2.5 m* Nov-Mar. Similar erect habit to *x bodnantense*, but the very fragrant flowers are much paler in colour and the spring 'flushes' are accompanied by the pale coppery-green embryo leaves, which give it an added attraction. It looks particularly good when planted against a dark background such as a conifer.

141

V. opulus 'Compactum' ⚥ ◯ ht: 4 ft *1.25 m* dist: 3 ft *1 m* May-Jun. A nice dwarf form of the rather larger guelder rose with sharply toothed maple-like leaves. The white flower heads are composed of showy ray florets which surround the inner fertile flowers. Large bunches of glistening red fruits follow in autumn.

The cultivar 'Xanthocarpum' has golden translucent fruits, and the two cultivars planted together look very good when in fruit.

V. plicatum 'Mariesii' ⚥ ≢ ht: 7 ft *2.25 m* dist: 7-8 ft *2.25-2.5 m* May. Flat tiers of branches covered in snow-white flowers make this an outstanding garden plant, which even when not in flower remains of interest for the way it contrasts with other plant forms.

V. rhytidophyllum ⚘ ◯ ht: 12 ft *3.5 m* dist: 10 ft *3 m* May-Jun. A fast-growing shrub with large dark-green, heavily veined leaves, white-felted beneath. These can look very sad and drooping in the winter, especially during prolonged cold periods, but they soon recover on warm sunny days. The felt-covered flower buds, after sitting still all winter, finally open in late spring to large 6 in (15 cm) dull white flower heads. The fruits are small, red at first then black. A really bold plant for the larger garden.

V. tinus ⚘ ◯ ht: 9 ft *2.75 m* dist. 7-8 ft *2.25-2.5 m* Nov-May. The Laurustinus, as it is commonly known, is perhaps the most commonly planted of the viburnums. Its dark evergreen leaves are one of its major attractions. For the bees and beekeeper, however, it is the round pink-budded flower heads which open to white from early winter to spring that make it a particular favourite. The small blue-black whortleberry-like clusters of fruits are most attractive and are often still present when the new flowers open. The cultivar 'Eve Price' is slightly less vigorous and has smaller leaves.

In less exposed and severely cold districts the variegated form, 'Variegatum', is worth a try and is a genuinely showy plant with creamy yellow leaves.

Viola (Pansies and/or Violets) Nec. ◯

The larger-flowered garden types are generally known as pansies, whilst the smaller ones are often referred to as violets, but there are no hard and fast distinctions. All have rather flat, nodding or horizontal flowers, often fragrant, with velvet-textured conspicuously veined petals. The flowers, with their hairy throats and finger-like nectaries tucked away to the side and base of the stamens, make honey bee access to nectar anything but easy, but they are worked by bees, especially those plants with short nectary spurs.

Most of the pansies have a small eye in a contrasting colour, and some are cultivated specifically for their face-like or fringe markings, in a variety of colours.

The summer-flowering cultivars, although very showy, will not be first choice for the honey bee when there is a wide choice of other flowers, so they are not described here.

'Universal' Bien. ht: 9 in *23 cm* dist: 9 in *23 cm* Sep-May, full sun, semi-shade. The introduction of the 'Universal' range must be one of the major triumphs for plant breeders in the last ten years, for they are quite outstanding and given a relatively mild winter will produce their 3-4 in (7.5-10 cm) flowers continuously for twelve months. The colour range is good and there are separate white, apricots, blues (pale and dark), yellows, purples and reds. 'Apricot' is a particular favourite, with its rich deep coloration.

'Floral Dance' Bien. ht: 9 in *23 cm* dist: 9 in *23 cm* Sep-May, full sun, semi-shade. Flowers somewhat smaller. Available in a wide range of colours, all with a largish irregular black eye.

Both the above cultivars should be sown outdoors or under glass in May/June, for planting out in their final locations in September/October.

The violets are rather more subtle than the pansies, and conjure up pictures of deliciously fragrant Mothers' Day posies edged with primroses.

V. cornuta H. ht: 4 in *10 cm* dist: 9 in *23 cm* Apr-Sep, semi-shade. Available in white, pale-blue and dark purple forms, flowering from spring to late autumn.

V. cucullata 'Freckles' H. ht: 6 in *15 cm* dist: 9 in

23 cm Apr-May, semi-shade. Very pale blue ground colour, almost covered with small purple freckles. A really stunning colour combination. It is difficult to believe that each flower has not been painstakingly hand-painted.

V. odorata (Sweet Violet) H. ht: 4 in *10 cm* dist: 6 in *15 cm* Apr-May, semi-shade. The fragrance and deep violet colour of the flower are simply incomparable. Several named cultivars are available.

V. labradorica 'Purpurea' H. ht: 4 in *10 cm* dist: 9-12 in *23-30 cm* dry, semi-shade. Lilac-mauve flowers set against dark purple leaves. Handsome, but can be invasive.

Weigela Nec. Shr. Ⴑ ◌
full sun, semi-shade
One of the earliest of the summer-flowering shrubs to show its colours, which it does year after year without any fuss. Summer starts for me when I see clusters of the funnel-shaped flowers, each with their fuchsia-like pistil and great knoblike stigma. A smaller, second flush of flowers may be produced in the autumn. The flower tubes are wide enough for honey bee access, but they may gain entry from the side through holes made by bumble bees. Flower size will deteriorate if the plants are left unpruned, thus making bee access more difficult, so thin out the old flowered shoots in February each year. I have four cultivars in my own garden and wish I had space for more.

W. florida ht: 6 ft *2 m* dist: 6 ft *2 m* May-Jun. Flower buds rose-pink at first, paler within.

'Foliis Purpureis' ht: 4 ft *1.25 m* dist: 4 ft *1.25 m* May-Jun. Slower growing than the species, its attractive dark purple foliage contrasts nicely with the deep-pink flowers. It looks particularly good when planted next to variegated shrubs. I have this cultivar and the next listed planted together.

'Variegata' ht: 4 ft *1.25 m* dist: 4 ft *1.25 m* May-Jun. This must be one of the very best variegated shrubs, with its wide creamy-yellow leaf variegation which in cold weather may partially turn a delicate pink. Flowers pale pink.

W. x 'Bristol Ruby' ht: 4 ft *1.25 m* dist: 4 ft *1.25 m* May-Jun. Brilliant ruby-red flowers. A superb plant, worthy of the Royal Horticultural Society's ultimate accolades: Award of Merit and Award of Garden Merit, received in 1954 and 1969 respectively.

W. middendorffiana ht: 4 ft *1.25 m* dist: 4 ft *1.25 m* Apr-May. Yellow foxglove-like flowers, unusual in the genus, with dark orange markings on the lower lobes. Needs some shelter from wind and sun.

6 Pruning

On balance, far more harm is done to plants by pruning than by just leaving them alone — after all, there is virtually no pruning in nature, except by browsing animals and wind damage. In far too many cases pruning is done in order to contain plants which are too vigorous for their locations, and this should be a major reason for very careful selection of the right plant for the right situation. In addition, pruning is carried out for the following reasons:

1. to encourage larger, better-quality flowers, e.g. *Buddleia davidii* and all roses.

2. to 'shape' plants to the required form. To my mind its severest form, topiary, is akin to the ancient and barbaric Chinese custom of foot-binding. There are, however, 'degrees' of shaping, and there are few gardens where this practice does not have to be resorted to at times.

3. to remove diseased or dead shoots and branches to prevent further infection of healthy parts. Be sure to burn diseased material.

Finally, do bear in mind that the vast bulk of trees and shrubs do not require any regular pruning. If in doubt, leave well alone.

Pruning tools and their use

A pruning knife is a very good tool for removing or pruning back shoots up to ½

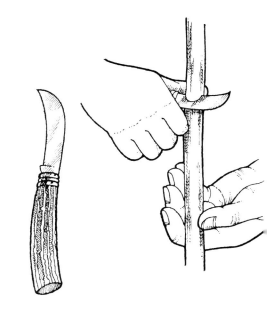

Using a pruning knife

in (1.3 cm) or so in diameter, but it does demand a good degree of practice and skill and it can be quite dangerous. So, if using this method, make certain that the hand supporting the branch to be pruned is in the opposite direction to the 'follow through' of the proposed cut. Contrary to expectation, it is in fact very much safer to draw the knife *towards* rather than away from you. Do not expect to master the technique in under 3-4 hours. It is perhaps not an ideal pruning method for the amateur gardener, however keen he may be.

Secateurs, also, should not be used for branches much larger in diameter than ½ in (1.3 cm), as otherwise crushing of the tissues with subsequent die-back is very likely to occur. The anvil-type secateurs are more likely, in my opinion, to crush tissues than the overlapping blade or bypass types. The so-called long-arm pruners or loppers certainly give greater leverage but do not overcome the crushing problem.

Whichever type of secateur or lopper is used, always make sure the branch is well

144

WRONG   RIGHT   WRONG   RIGHT

Pruning plants with alternate and opposite buds

in the centre of the blades rather than just inside the tips. Whether using a knife or secateurs always cut to a bud or buds. Where the buds are opposite, as in *Buddleia* and *Cornus*, a straight cut just above the buds is required. Where the buds alternate, as in *Forsythia*, then a sloping cut starting just above the bud and sloping down slightly away from it, is normal.

Saws are best used for any shoots over a ½ in (1.3 cm) in diameter, and these can be of the curved 'Grecian' pattern (very useful for making cuts in difficult places), or the tapered double-edged type with fine teeth on one edge and coarse for larger branches on the other. Always support the piece to be cut off with the other hand, to prevent partially severed branches falling and ripping the bark from the main stem.

Do not be tempted to make flush cuts when removing side branches from the main stem of trees, since this will usually leave a very large scar (as shown in the diagram) which will be slow to heal. On the other hand, do not go so far in the other direction that you leave a stump to die back.

Although it has been standard practice in the past to paint over any pruning cuts larger than ½ in (1.3 cm) in diameter with a special wound sealant, it is now generally accepted that this treatment may actually increase the risk of die-back. For aesthetic reasons (dark brown being a more natural colour than the white of a cut branch) wound painting is still practised.

Principles of pruning

As a student I remember spending many weary hours learning techniques for pruning a massive range of plants. I would have been better employed learning to apply the general principles of pruning as set out below — for armed with these it is difficult to go too far wrong.

Detailed descriptions of fruit trees and

Grecian and double-edged saws

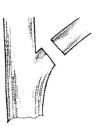
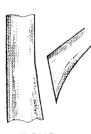

RIGHT   WRONG   WRONG

Pruning a side branch

145

bush pruning are beyond the scope of this book, but some information has been given in the plant descriptions.

The shrubs are far and away the largest group with pruning requirements. All shrubs fall broadly into one of three pruning groups. This division is a simplistic approach, but one which should nevertheless ensure that you do not go too far wrong. When you have identified which pruning groups your plants belong to, then you will at least know when to prune. This is vital, because pruning at the wrong time can remove all the potential flowers or fruit. For detailed information on individual genera refer to one of the many excellent and well illustrated books dealing with the subject, such as the Royal Horticultural Society's *Concise Encyclopedia of Gardening Techniques*.

How to use our pruning guide

Using the plant lists, look for the following information on the plant you want to prune:

flowering period? (e.g. Jun-Oct)
evergreen or deciduous? (🌿 or ⅄)
does it have attractive fruit or berries?
❦

The first pruning cuts should always aim at removing dead and diseased shoots. Having done this you are now ready to move on to the instructions given in the group to which the plant belongs.

Group 1 Spring-flowering, deciduous and evergreen shrubs (flower up to June in UK), e.g. *Forsythia, Ribes, Cytisus*, rambling roses, some *Clematis* (check with plant lists), *Mahonia, Rhododendron, Erica australis, E. x darleyensis* and *E. mediterranea*, etc.

Prune immediately after the flowers have faded.

Shorten the stems which have carried flowers.
Most evergreens are best left unpruned, so limit your efforts here to periodic thinning.

Group 2 Summer-flowering deciduous and evergreen shrubs (flower from June onwards in UK), e.g. *Potentilla, Weigela*, roses (except ramblers), some *Hypericum* (see plant lists), *Cistus, Calluna, Erica cinerea, tetralix* and *vagans, Rosmarinus, Thymus*, etc.

Prune in February-March, just before new growth commences.
Cut back some of the older shoots that carry little in the way of new growth. This should encourage vigour.
Trim back some of the remaining shoots.
Most evergreens are again in this group, and are best left unpruned, so limit your efforts once more to periodic thinning.

Group 3 Spring or summer-flowering shrubs that bear berries or attractive fruits (deciduous or evergreen). This group of plants presents the gardener with a real dilemma. If he prunes after flowering, colourful autumn fruits may be removed (this may not worry the beekeeper too much), and if he prunes after the berries fall or are eaten, flower buds may be removed in the process. This may concern the beekeeper a good deal more.

Try always to plant this type of shrub at an adequate spacing to prevent the need for excessive pruning.
Do not leave pruning until major 'surgery' is required. Little and often is best.
For the beekeeper: some pruning immediately after flowering is the best bet, if it is required. Thin out weak shoots and remove overcrowded ones.

7 Use of pesticides

Every gardener will find pests and disease affecting the plants in the garden and, if the attack is of sufficient importance, will have to use pesticides to combat it. The word 'pesticide' is used not only to cover 'insecticides' but also 'herbicides', 'fungicides', 'acaricides', and many other classes of chemicals which do not normally present a threat to the honey bee. Some acaricides are used in the hive to control parasitic mites such as Acarine or Varroa, and are harmless to the bee if used correctly.

Obviously, those chemicals developed specifically for the control of insects are most likely to cause problems for your bees. Fungicides and herbicides are not formulated in the same way, and this, coupled with the fact that there is normally no need to use them on crops or weeds when they are in flower (which is of course the time when bees are most at risk), means they are usually less dangerous. However, there is a risk in using herbicides on low-growing plants, even when not in flower, because honey bees often collect water from herbage near, or a short distance from, the hives. There have been cases of bees being poisoned by collecting freshly applied herbicide. If it is necessary to use herbicides, they are best applied after the bees have finished flying for the day, preferably at a time when a heavy dew is unlikely to occur, so that the chemicals will be absorbed before morning. All chemicals should be used carefully, following the instructions on the label and the suggestions which follow.

Perhaps not everyone is as lucky as I am (or as forgiving of pest damage), but in my own garden, which contains quite a wide range of plants, I manage with no more than four insecticide sprays a year (using only three different materials): one for my roses and the remaining three for my brassicas. The chemicals I use are permethrin and malathion (e.g. PBI Crop Saver) for caterpillars on brassicas, and dimethoate (e.g. Murphy Systemic Insecticide) for aphids on roses. Both materials are *very poisonous* to bees but I apply them very carefully, following the guide lines I give below, and have never had any problems.

A scan of the pesticides on your local garden centre shelves will quickly bring you to the conclusion that there are very few materials which can control the two pests mentioned above that are *not* harmful to bees. Products containing pirimicarb, however, *are* harmless to bees, ladybirds, lacewings and other useful predators and give good control of aphids on a wide range of plants. The ICI product

147

Use of Pesticides

'Roseclear' contains pirimicarb and two fungicides to give safe control of aphids, mildew and blackspot on roses. For cabbage white butterfly caterpillars try *Bacillus thuringiensis*. This material is a microbial insecticide containing toxic protein and bacterial spores. It only attacks moth or butterfly caterpillars and is quite harmless to bees and man; in fact, it has been used for the control of waxmoth in stored comb from honey bee colonies. The only drawback this material has when used on plants is that it works on contact, so that very thorough wetting of the foliage is necessary to ensure all the pests are wetted.

If red-spider mite is a problem, then derris can be used, preferably in liquid form. This will also control caterpillar, thrips, raspberry beetle and many other pests. It is extremely poisonous to fish, and since very many gardens have a pond or pool of some description great care should be exercised when using it.

Control of major and common pests with 'safe' materials

Pest/Disease	Material	Comments
Aphids (Greenfly, including Black Bean aphid)	Pirimicarb	Good wetting of plants essential.
Caterpillars (on trees, shrubs, brassicas, etc.)	Bacillus thuringiensis	Good wetting of plants essential
Flea beetle (seedling brassicas and wallflowers)	Derris	Good wetting of plants essential.
Gooseberry sawfly		
Raspberry beetle		
Red-spider (on wide range of crops)		
Blackspot (roses)	Triforine	Systemic, complete wetting not essential
Scab (apples)		
Mildew (roses, apple, blackcurrant, gooseberry)	Bupirimate	

148

Guidelines for safe use of pesticides

1. *Do not spray unnecessarily* Do not spray at the first sight of a greenfly, caterpillar or any other pest. Handpicking or squashing these pests can be quite effective in the small garden, and it is surprising, if one persists, how often a full-scale attack is averted.

2. *Do not spray plants in bloom* Never spray plants which are in flower with chemicals which are classified as harmful or dangerous to bees. Remember, too, that although the crop itself may not be in bloom, weeds directly beneath it may be in flower and if these are attractive to bees then you will still have a problem.

3. *Always choose the least toxic chemical* When a pesticide must be used to stop an attack by pests, always use the one among the recommended chemicals for the job which has the lowest toxicity and is least harmful to bees.

4. *Apply pesticides only after the bees have stopped flying* This also has the advantage that in many cases any wind will have abated and spray drift will be reduced to a minimum.

5. *Use the lowest possible pressure when applying pesticides* Some of the larger, more 'professional' knapsack sprayers can be adjusted for pressure. With smaller models it is simply a case of not pumping too vigorously and avoiding producing the small droplets which are prone to drifting, on even the lightest breeze.

6. *Do not use aerosols out of doors* Aerosols are designed for use indoors. The tiny droplets are so small they will remain suspended in the air for a considerable time, and if used out of doors will drift widely on even the calmest day.

7. *Always read the label carefully before spraying* Read the label and comply with the directions. Never increase the dosage on the principle that 'a double dose will do twice as much good' — often it will be disastrous.

The beekeeper will recognize cases of poisoning when large numbers of bees die at the hive entrance. This is not caused by something the amateur gardener has done; it is characteristic of the effect of spraying large areas of crop, particularly from the air. Study of a beekeeping textbook will give details of the detection of poisoning and what to do should it happen. The position with regard to pesticide poisoning of bees is improving all the time, as farmers and growers become more aware of the importance of the conservation of wild life, and the need to spray with care and forethought.

Index

Only a few cultivars are listed here. Several hundred are described in the texts associated with their related species. Page numbers in italics refer to illustrations.

150

151

Index